AS-Level
Physics

The Revision Guide

Exam Board: OCR B (Advancing Physics)

Editors:
Amy Boutal, Julie Wakeling, Sarah Williams

Contributors
Tony Alldridge, Jane Cartwright, Peter Cecil, Peter Clarke, Mark A. Edwards, Barbara Mascetti, John Myers, Andy Williams

Proofreaders:
Mark A. Edwards, Glenn Rogers

Published by Coordination Group Publications Ltd.

With thanks to Science Photo Library for permission to reproduce the photographs used on pages 30 and 31.

With thanks to Jan Greenway for the copyright research.

ISBN: 978 1 84762 132 0

Groovy website: www.cgpbooks.co.uk
Jolly bits of clipart from CorelDRAW®
Printed by Elanders Ltd, Newcastle upon Tyne.

Based on the classic CGP style created by Richard Parsons.

Contents

The Scientific Process

'How Science Works' is all about the scientific process — how we develop and test scientific ideas.
It's what scientists do all day, every day (well, except at coffee time — never come between a scientist and their coffee).

Scientists Come Up with **Theories** — Then **Test Them**...

Science tries to explain **how** and **why** things happen — it **answers questions**. It's all about seeking and gaining **knowledge** about the world around us. Scientists do this by **asking** questions and **suggesting** answers and then **testing** them, to see if they're correct — this is the **scientific process**.

1) **Ask** a question — make an **observation** and ask **why or how** it happens. E.g. what is the nature of light?

2) **Suggest** an answer, or part of an answer, by forming:
   - a **theory** (a possible **explanation** of the observations) e.g. light is a wave.
   - a **model** (a **simplified picture** of what's physically going on)

3) Make a **prediction** or **hypothesis** — a **specific testable statement**, based on the theory, about what will happen in a test situation. E.g. light should interfere and diffract.

4) Carry out a **test** — to provide **evidence** that will support the prediction, or help disprove it. E.g. Young's double-slit experiment.

The evidence supported Quentin's Theory of Flammable Burps.

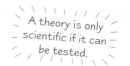

A theory is only scientific if it can be tested.

...Then They **Tell** Everyone About Their **Results**...

The results are **published** — scientists need to let others know about their work. Scientists publish their results in **scientific journals**. These are just like normal magazines, only they contain **scientific reports** (called papers) instead of the latest celebrity gossip.

1) Scientific reports are similar to the **lab write-ups** you do in school. And just as a lab write-up is **reviewed** (marked) by your teacher, reports in scientific journals undergo **peer review** before they're published.

2) The report is sent out to **peers** — other scientists that are experts in the **same area**. They examine the data and results, and if they think that the conclusion is reasonable it's **published**. This makes sure that work published in scientific journals is of a **good standard**.

3) But peer review **can't guarantee** the science is **correct** — other scientists still need to **reproduce** it.

4) Sometimes **mistakes** are made and bad work is published. Peer review **isn't perfect** but it's probably the best way for scientists to self-regulate their work and to publish **quality reports**.

...Then **Other Scientists** Will **Test** the Theory Too

Other scientists read the published theories and results, and try to **test the theory** themselves. This involves:

- Repeating the **exact same experiments**.
- Using the theory to make **new predictions** and then testing them with **new experiments**.

If the **Evidence** Supports a Theory, It's **Accepted** — for Now

1) If all the experiments in all the world provide evidence to back it up, the theory is thought of as **scientific 'fact'** (for now).

2) But they never become **totally undisputable** fact. Scientific **breakthroughs or advances** could provide new ways to question and test the theory, which could lead to **new evidence** that **conflicts** with the current evidence. Then the testing starts all over again...

And this, my friend, is the **tentative nature of scientific knowledge** — it's always **changing** and **evolving**.

The Scientific Process

So scientists need evidence to back up their theories. They get it by carrying out experiments, and when that's not possible they carry out studies. But why bother with science at all? We want to know as much as possible so we can use it to try and improve our lives (and because we're nosey).

Evidence Comes From Controlled Lab Experiments...

1) Results from **controlled experiments** in **laboratories** are **great**.
2) A lab is the easiest place to **control variables** so that they're all **kept constant** (except for the one you're investigating).

For example, finding the resistance of a piece of material by altering the voltage across the material and measuring the current flowing through it (see p.18). All other variables need to be kept the same, e.g. the dimensions of the piece of material being tested, as they may also affect its resistance.

... That You can Draw Meaningful Conclusions From

1) You always need to make your experiments as **controlled** as possible so you can be confident that any effects you see are linked to the variable you're changing.
2) If you do find a relationship, you need to be careful what you conclude. You need to decide whether the effect you're seeing is **caused** by changing a variable, or whether the two are just **correlated**.

"Right Geoff, you can start the experiment now... I've stopped time..."

Society Makes Decisions Based on Scientific Evidence

1) Lots of scientific work eventually leads to **important discoveries** or breakthroughs that could **benefit humankind**.
2) These results are **used by society** (that's you, me and everyone else) to **make decisions** — about the way we live, what we eat, what we drive, etc.
3) All sections of society use scientific evidence to make decisions, e.g. politicians use it to devise policies and individuals use science to make decisions about their own lives.

Other factors can **influence** decisions about science or the way science is used:

Economic factors

- Society has to consider the **cost** of implementing changes based on scientific conclusions — e.g. the cost of reducing the UK's carbon emissions to limit the human contribution to **global warming**.
- Scientific research is often **expensive**. E.g. in areas such as astronomy, the Government has to **justify** spending money on a new telescope rather than pumping money into, say, the **NHS** or **schools**.

Social factors

- **Decisions** affect **people's lives** — e.g. when looking for a site to build a **nuclear power station**, you need to consider how it would affect the lives of the people in the **surrounding area**.

Environmental factors

- Many scientists suggest that building **wind farms** would be a **cheap** and **environmentally friendly** way to generate electricity in the future. But some people think that because **wind turbines** can **harm wildlife** such as birds and bats, other methods of generating electricity should be used.

So there you have it — how science works...

Hopefully these pages have given you a nice intro to how science works, e.g. what scientists do to provide you with 'facts'. You need to understand this, as you're expected to know how science works yourself — for the exam and for life.

The Nature of Waves

This section's all about what happens when you take a picture with your mobile and send it to your mate Dave... with a few other minor details... it's all waves waves waves.

Waves are used in Imaging and Signalling

Pretty much all information is transferred by waves. Whenever you create an image or send a signal, it'll be waves that do the lackey work. Here are just a few examples of where they're used:

1) **Medical imaging** — e.g. ultrasound scans build up an image of a fetus by detecting reflected **ultrasound waves**.

2) **Communications** — e.g. your mobile phone sends and receives **microwaves** that carry the signal containing that all-important text message.

3) **Scientific imaging** — e.g. light waves from stars and galaxies take billions of years to reach the Earth, and are used to make an image that can be recorded electronically.

4) **Seeing** — anything you see, from stars to the cat being sick on your nicest pair of jeans, is thanks to millions of light waves hitting your retinas and forming an image.

5) **Heat cameras** sense infrared waves being emitted by the hot thing you're looking at. Infrared radiation is also the type of electromagnetic wave that carries the signal from your TV remote control to your telly to switch over to your favourite soap...

A Wave Transfers Energy Away from Its Source

A **progressive** (moving) wave carries **energy** and usually information from one place to another **without transferring any material**. Here are some ways you can tell waves carry energy:

1) Electromagnetic waves cause things to **heat up**.
2) **X-rays** and **gamma rays** knock electrons out of their orbits, causing **ionisation**.
3) Loud **sounds** make things **vibrate**.
4) **Wave power** can be used to **generate electricity**.
5) Since waves carry energy away, the **source** of the wave **loses energy**.

Here are all the bits of a Wave you Need to Know

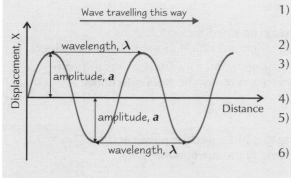

1) **Displacement, X, metres** — how far a **point** on the wave has **moved** from its **undisturbed position**.

2) **Amplitude, a, metres** — **maximum displacement**.

3) **Wavelength, λ, metres** — the **length** of **one whole wave**, from **crest** to **crest** or **trough** to **trough**.

4) **Period, T, seconds** — the **time taken** for a **whole vibration**.

5) **Frequency, f, hertz** — the **number** of **vibrations per second** passing a given **point**.

6) **Phase difference** — the amount by which **one** wave **lags behind another** wave. Measured in **degrees** or **radians**. See page 36.

Waves Can Be Reflected and Refracted

Reflection — the wave is **bounced back** when it **hits a boundary**. E.g. you can see the reflection of light in mirrors. The reflection of water waves can be demonstrated in a ripple tank.

Refraction — the wave **changes direction** as it enters a **different medium**. The change in direction is a result of the wave slowing down or speeding up (see page 8).

The Nature of Waves

The **Frequency** is the **Inverse** of the **Period**

$$Frequency = \frac{1}{period}$$

It's that simple.
Get the **units** straight: **1 Hz = 1 s⁻¹**.

Wave Speed, Frequency and Wavelength are Linked by the Wave Equation

Wave speed can be measured just like the speed of anything else:

$$Speed \ (v) = \frac{distance\ moved\ (d)}{time\ taken\ (t)}$$

*Remember, you're not measuring how fast a physical point (like one molecule of rope) moves. You're measuring how fast a point on the **wave pattern** moves.*

Learn the **Wave Equation**...

Speed of wave (v) = wavelength (λ) × frequency (f)

$$v = \lambda f$$

You need to be able to rearrange this equation for v, λ or f.

... and How to **Derive** it

You can work out the **wave equation** by imagining **how long** it takes for the **crest** of a wave to **move** across a **distance** of **one wavelength**. The **distance travelled** is λ. **By definition**, the **time taken** to travel **one whole wavelength** is the **period** of the wave, which is equal to **1/f**.

$$Speed \ (v) = \frac{distance\ moved\ (d)}{time\ taken\ (t)} \quad \longrightarrow \quad Speed \ (v) = \frac{distance\ moved\ (\lambda)}{time\ taken\ (1/f)}$$

Learn to recognise when to use $v = \lambda f$ and when to use $v = d/t$. Look at which variables are mentioned in the question.

Practice Questions

Q1   Does a wave carry matter **or** energy from one place to another?

Q2   Diffraction and interference are two wave properties. Write down two more.

Q3   Give the units of frequency, displacement and amplitude.

Q4   Write down the equation connecting v, λ and f.

Exam Question

Q1   A buoy floating on the sea takes 6 seconds to rise and fall once (complete a full period of oscillation).
The difference in height between the buoy at its lowest and highest points is 1.2 m, and waves pass it at a speed of 3 ms⁻¹.

(a) How long are the waves?   [2 marks]

(b) What is the amplitude of the waves?   [1 mark]

ARRRGH... waves are everywhere — there's no escape...

Even just reading this is one instance of using waves in signalling and imaging. A bunch of light waves are being reflected off this page and carrying the 'signal' to your retinas... which they pass on to the brain and ta da — you can see. Clever huh?

Transverse Waves and Polarisation

From communications to photography, polarised waves are really useful. Which is why you get to learn all about 'em...

All Electromagnetic Waves are Transverse Waves

1) **A transverse wave** is a wave where the the **vibration** is at **right angles** to the wave's **direction** of travel.

2) All **electromagnetic waves** are **transverse**. Other examples of transverse waves are **ripples** on water and waves on **ropes**.

3) There are **two** main ways of **drawing** transverse waves:

①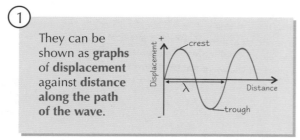

They can be shown as **graphs** of **displacement** against **distance** along the path of the wave.

②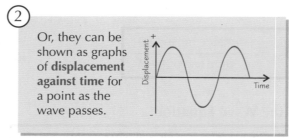

Or, they can be shown as graphs of **displacement against time** for a point as the wave passes.

Both sorts of graph often give the **same shape**, so make sure you check out the label on the **x-axis**. Displacements **upwards** from the centre line are given a **+ sign**. Displacements downwards are given a **– sign**.

4) Not all waves are transverse, **sound** for example is a **longitudinal** wave — the vibrations are along the wave's direction of travel.

A Polarised Wave only Oscillates in One Direction

1) If you **shake a rope** to make a **wave** you can move your hand **up and down** or **side to side** or in a **mixture** of directions — it still makes a **transverse wave**.

2) But if you try to pass **waves in a rope** through a **vertical fence**, the wave will only get through if the **vibrations are vertical**. The fence filters out vibration in other directions. This is called **polarising** the wave.

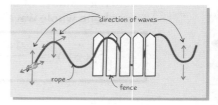

Electromagnetic Radiation can be Polarised

1) **Electromagnetic radiation** (e.g. light) is made up of two transverse waves. (The things vibrating are electric and magnetic fields.)

2) A **polarising filter** acts a bit like the fence. Light that has passed through the polarising filter will only be vibrating in one direction.

3) If you have two polarising filters at **right angles** to each other, then **no** light will get through as all directions of vibration will be blocked.

4) Polarisation **can only happen** for **transverse** waves. The fact that you can polarise light is one **proof** that it's a transverse wave.

When Light Reflects it is Partially Polarised

1) Rotating a **polarising filter** in a beam of light shows the fraction of the light that is vibrating in each **direction**.

2) If you direct a beam of unpolarised light at a reflective surface then view the **reflected ray** through a polarising filter, the intensity of light leaving the filter **changes** with the **orientation** of the filter.

3) The intensity changes because light is **partially polarised** when it is **reflected**.

4) This effect comes in handy in photography (see next page).

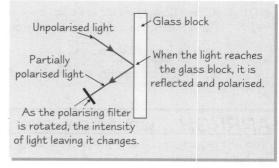

Unpolarised light

Glass block

Partially polarised light

When the light reaches the glass block, it is reflected and polarised.

As the polarising filter is rotated, the intensity of light leaving it changes.

Transverse Waves and Polarisation

Polarised Light Has Many Uses

Polarised light is used a lot in communications and imaging. Here are just a few examples...

If you walk down the street and look up at the **TV aerials** on people's houses, you'll see that the **rods** (the sticky-out bits) on them are all **horizontal**. The reason for this is that **TV signals** are **polarised** by the orientation of the **rods** on the **broadcasting aerial**. To receive a strong signal, you have to **line up** the rods on the **receiving aerial** with the **rods** on the **transmitting aerial** — if they aren't aligned, the signal strength will be lower.

It's the **same** with **radio** — if you try **tuning a radio** and then **moving** the **aerial** around, your signal will **come and go** as the transmitting and receiving aerials go in and out of **alignment**.

Some **communications satellites** use different polarisations for signals in the same frequency band to help reduce the amount of **interference** between the signals.

It's not just our communications signals it's used for — polarisation plays a crucial part in nature too. **Bees** (and other insects) use polarised light to navigate, so when they find a good pollen spot, they can direct the other bees back at the hive.

Cor... wait 'til I tell the lads where I found this beauty...

CD players use a polarising crystal to transmit light polarised in one direction, and reflect light polarised in any other direction.

The fact that reflected light is partly polarised means photographers can use polarising lenses to remove **unwanted reflections** in the pictures they take. It's also why skiers wear **Polaroid sunglasses** — they block the **glare** of sunlight reflected off the snow.

Practice Questions

Q1 Give one example of a transverse wave.

Q2 Describe the direction of vibrations in a transverse wave.

Q3 What is a polarised wave? How can you polarise a wave?

Q4 Give one example where polarised waves are used to transmit information.

Q5 Describe why polarising sunglasses cut out glare from road surfaces.

Exam Questions

Q1 In an experiment, light is shone through a disc of a crystal called "Iceland spar". The beam of light is less bright when it emerges from the crystal than when it enters. Next, a second identical disc of Iceland spar is placed in front of the first. The first disc is held steady while the second is rotated (in the plane of the disc). The intensity of light emerging changes as the second disc rotates. At two points in each rotation, no light gets through at all.

Explain the results of these experiments. You may use a diagram to help your answer.   [5 marks]

Q2 Give one example of an application of polarisation and explain how it works.   [2 marks]

Polarised light — it's cool to the extreme...

One of my favourite uses of polarisation is 3D films. Each lens in 3D specs lets a different polarisation of light through, so a slightly different image is sent to each of your eyes. The brain takes these images and makes a 3D image, to give you the full effect of a dinosaur about to chomp off your head by lunging at you from the screen. Which is a good thing...

Forming Images with Lenses

Astronomers use focal lengths, opticians use powers. Either way, you need to know how to deal with lens powers...

Refraction Happens when a Wave Changes Speed at a Boundary

1) When a ray of light meets a boundary between one medium and another, some of its energy is **reflected** back into the first medium and the rest of it is **transmitted** through into the second medium.

2) If the light meets the boundary at an angle to the normal, the transmitted ray is bent or "**refracted**" as it travels at a **different speed** in each medium.
The more **optically dense** a material is, the more slowly light travels in it.

3) The **absolute refractive index** of a material, *n*, is the **ratio** between the **speed of light** in a **vacuum**, *c*, and the speed of light in that **material**, *v*.

$$n = \frac{c}{v}$$

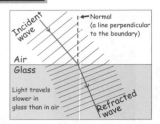

Converging Lenses Change the Curvature of Wavefronts

1) **Lenses** change the curvature of wavefronts by **refraction**.

2) A lens **adds curvature** to waves as they pass through it. If waves are uncurved before passing through the lens, and parallel to the lens axis, they will be given spherical curvature, centred on the **focus** (or **focal point**) of the lens.

3) The lens curves the wavefronts by **slowing down** the light travelling through the middle of the lens for longer than light at the lens edges. All points on a wavefront takes the **same amount of time** to get to the focus point (see p 53).

4) The **focal length**, *f*, is the distance between the **lens axis** and the **focus**.

5) The **more powerful** (thicker) the lens, the more **strongly** it will **curve** the wavefronts that travel through it — so the **shorter** its **focal length**.

6) The **power** of a lens with focal length *f* m is: where lens power is measured in **dioptres**, D.

$$P = \frac{1}{f}$$

7) The curvature of a wave is defined as:

$$\text{curvature} = \frac{1}{\text{radius of curvature}}$$

So the **amount of curvature** a lens adds to a wave passing through it is 1/**f**... which is just the **power** of the lens.

You can also show image formation with **ray diagrams**.

You can use the Lens Equation to Find Where an Image Will be Formed

1) The distances between the lens, the image and the source are related to each other by **the lens equation**:

$$\frac{1}{v} = \frac{1}{u} + \frac{1}{f}$$

u = distance between object and lens axis,
v = distance between image and lens axis,
f = focal length.

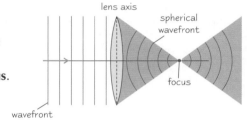

2) You always measure the **distances** from the **lens axis**, and count distances to the **right** as **positive**, and distances to the **left** as **negative** — just like when you're drawing graphs.

3) The lens equation also tells you about **curvature**.

4) So, if you've got a **distant source**, the wavefronts will be **flat** (1/*u* = 0) and the lens will give them a curvature of 1/*f*. Easy.

curvature after	= curvature before	+ curvature added by lens
(1/*v*)	(1/*u*)	(1/*f*)

5) If the source is at the **focal point** of the lens, you'll probably have a **negatively curved** (as the radius is a negative distance) wavefront before the light reaches the lens, which will be made **flat** once its passed through the lens.

6) For sources in between, the wavefronts before and after will be curved, and have a difference in curvature of 1/*f*.

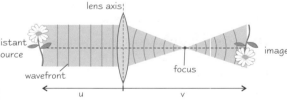

7) Don't forget that you can also draw all this in the form of **light rays** being 'bent' by the lens. It's just a different way of thinking about it — you still use the lens equation in exactly the same way.

Forming Images with Lenses

Example

An image of Mabel the cow is being projected onto a screen 80 cm from a 3.25 D lens. How far must the picture slide of Mabel be from the lens?

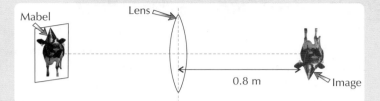

$P = \dfrac{1}{f} = 3.25$ D, $v = 80$ cm $= 0.8$ m

Rearrange the lens equation: $\dfrac{1}{u} = \dfrac{1}{v} - \dfrac{1}{f} = \dfrac{1}{0.8} - 3.25 = 1.25 - 3.25 = -2$

$u = -\dfrac{1}{2} = -0.5$ m, so the slide must be $\underline{0.5\ \text{m}}$ from the lens.

A Lens Can Produce a **Magnified Image**

There are a couple of ways of measuring the magnification of a lens.
You just need to know about the **linear magnification**.

The **linear magnification** of a lens is $\boxed{m = \dfrac{\text{size of image}}{\text{size of object}}}$, which is equal to $\boxed{m = \dfrac{v}{u}}$.

Practice Questions

Q1   Define the focal length and power of a converging lens.

Q2   Write an equation to show how the object distance (*u*), image distance (*v*) and focal length (*f*) are related.

Q3   Describe what happens to wavefronts as they pass through a thin converging lens.

Q4   A wave passed through a thin converging lens with a focal length f.
     If the wavefronts had no curvature before entering the lens, what is their curvature after passing through the lens?

Exam Questions

Q1   (a) Define the *focal point* and the *focal length* of a converging lens.   [2 marks]

     (b) An object was placed 0.20 m in front of a converging lens of focal length 0.15 m.
        How far behind the lens was the image formed?   [2 marks]

Q2   The length of a seed is 12.5 mm. A lens is placed in front of the seed, so that the axis of the lens is parallel to the seed.
     An image of the seed is projected onto a screen. The image has a length of 47.2 mm.

     (a) Find the linear magnification of the lens.   [1 mark]

     (b) If the seed is 4 mm from the lens, how far is the screen from the lens?   [2 marks]

     (c) Calculate the power of the lens in dioptres.   [3 marks]

By the power of Grayskull... I HAVE THE POWER...

This is all fairly straightforward — just a few formulas. But it's a great one for experiment-based questions in the exam, so make sure you know how to deal with uncertainties and error bars. See page 74 for stuff on error analysis.

10

Information in Images

Don't panic if waves are getting a bit too much for you — it's time for something completely different.

A Single Binary Digit is Called a Bit

Decimal	Binary
0	0
1	1
2	10
3	11

1) The **binary number system**, like the **decimal** system, is a way of writing numbers.

2) The difference is that the **decimal** system uses **ten digits** (0-9) while the **binary** system only uses **two** (**0 and 1**). The table shows the first few values in each system.

3) The **zeros** and **ones** that make up binary numbers are called **binary digits** — a **single binary digit** is called a **bit**. A group of **eight binary digits** is called a **byte**.

The Binary System is used to Store Data in Computer Memory

1) When you **save** a file on your computer, the computer stores the data as a **string of bits**.

2) The **number of bits** in a string (I) determines how many **alternatives** that string can code for. For example, a **single** bit has only **two** alternatives (0 and 1), while one **byte** (eight bits) has **256** alternatives. The number of alternatives **doubles** with each additional bit, which means:

$$\text{Number of alternatives} = 2^{\text{Number of bits}} \text{ or } N = 2^I$$

Bytes are the smallest meaningful units of computer memory.

3) The **number of bits** you need depends on how many **alternatives** you want:

$$\text{Number of bits} = \log_2(\text{number of alternatives}) \text{ or } I = \log_2 N$$

For example, if you wanted to code for any letter of the **alphabet**, you'd need a string with **26 alternatives** — one for every letter. Substituting 26 into the **equation** gives $I = \log_2 26 \approx 4.7$ — so you'd need **five bits**.

Images Are Stored as Arrays of Binary Numbers

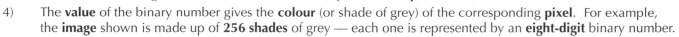

1) If you **zoom** in on part of a **digital photograph**, you'll see the individual **pixels** (squares of colour) that make up the image — check out the example on the right. →

2) When an **image** is stored in a digital camera (e.g. on a **memory card**) or on a **computer**, each pixel is represented by a **binary number**.

3) The **binary numbers** are stored in an **array**. They're arranged so that the **location** of a **number** in the grid **matches** the location in the photo of the **pixel** it describes.

4) The **value** of the binary number gives the **colour** (or shade of grey) of the corresponding **pixel**. For example, the **image** shown is made up of **256 shades** of grey — each one is represented by an **eight-digit** binary number.

5) In **coloured images**, each pixel can be described by **three** binary numbers — one for each of the **primary colours** of light (**red**, **green** and **blue**). The **length** of the binary numbers used depends on **how many** colours are needed.

Multiplying by a Fixed Value Improves Contrast

The **values** of the binary numbers that make up an **image** determine how it looks — if you **change** the **values**, you **change** the **image**. Take a look at the **example** below to see what happens.

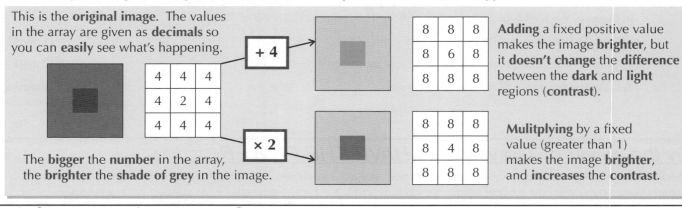

This is the **original image**. The values in the array are given as **decimals** so you can **easily** see what's happening.

4	4	4
4	2	4
4	4	4

The **bigger** the **number** in the array, the **brighter** the **shade of grey** in the image.

+ 4

8	8	8
8	6	8
8	8	8

Adding a fixed positive value makes the image **brighter**, but it **doesn't change** the **difference** between the **dark** and **light** regions (**contrast**).

× 2

8	8	8
8	4	8
8	8	8

Mulitplying by a fixed value (greater than 1) makes the image **brighter**, and **increases** the **contrast**.

Information in Images

Adding **False Colour** Highlights Features

In the example on the last page, a value of '**2**' in the array mapped to a **dark shade of grey** in the image, while a value of '**4**' mapped to a slightly **brighter shade**. But you could map '**2**' to a **dark shade of pink** and '**4**' to a **brighter shade** — or '**2**' to **orange** and '**4**' to **green**.

This process is called adding **false colour**. You can use **any** colours you like, but they're usually picked to **highlight certain features** — e.g. the **important features** could be made a really **bright** colour.

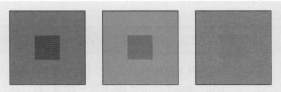

You can transform an image by changing the colours that the values in its array map to — not the array itself.

Replacing Pixels With the **Median** of their Neighbours **Reduces Noise**

This array would show a bright spot, in a uniform, darker region — the spot is probably noise.

2	3	2
1	12	2
2	2	1

→

2	3	2
1	2	2
2	2	1

Replacing the central value with the median of all nine values evens out the brightness of the region.

1) **Noise** is **unwanted interference** affecting a signal. In images this is usually **bright** or **dark** spots on the picture.

2) One way you can get rid of **noise** is to **replace** each pixel with the **median** of itself and the eight pixels surrounding it.

3) The result is that any '**odd**' (i.e. very **high** or very **low**) values are **removed** and the image is **smoother**.

The **Laplace Rule** is Used to **Find Edges**

If you're trying to work out if there is **something** in your **image** (rather than just a load of **noise**), finding any **edges** can be a really **useful** first step.

The **Laplace rule** is a method of **finding edges**. To apply the rule, you **multiply** a pixel by **four**, then **subtract** the value of the pixels immediately **above**, **below**, to the **left** and to the **right** of it.

The result is that any pixel **not** on an **edge** goes **black** — so you're left with **just** the edges.

The Laplace rule will only highlight an edge if there is a steep change in brightness (i.e. an edge). If the change is gradual (i.e. not an edge), the rule will smooth the change in brightness, making it less noticeable.

Practice Questions

Q1 What's the difference between a bit and a byte?

Q2 How can the brightness of an image be changed?

Q3 How can the contrast of an image by improved?

Q4 What is the Laplace rule used for? How do you apply it?

Exam Questions

Q1 The diagram shows part of an array that describes an image. The image is made up of 256 shades of grey — 0 represents black and 255 represents white.

100	99	100
97	185	98
101	101	98

(a) Sketch the image that this part of the array describes. [1 mark]

(b) Describe how noise can be removed from digital images. [1 mark]

(b) Apply this technique to the central value of the array shown. [1 mark]

Q2 A television can display 65 536 different colours.

(a) What is the minimum number of bits needed to store the colour of each pixel? [1 mark]

(b) How many bytes is this? [1 mark]

All this talk of bytes is making me hungry — mmm, tasty bites...

These two pages (and the next few) are a bit of a detour from the 'proper' Physics they taught in my day — where are all the complicated mathematical equations and boring diagrams to get lost in? It's just not right. If I had my way, I'd... well...

Sampling

You've just seen how information can be stored digitally, but what if you want to send that information?
And what if the information isn't digital to start with? So many questions — read on to find out the answers.

Analogue Signals Vary Continuously

1) **Digital signals**, like the images on the previous page, are represented by **binary numbers**.

2) The **values** that a **digital signal** can take depend on the **number of bits** used — e.g. a **one bit** signal can only take the values **0 and 1**, but a **one byte** signal can take **256 different values**.

3) **Analogue signals** are **not limited** in the values they can take — they **vary continuously**. For example, **speech** is an **analogue signal** — the **sound waves** produced **vary continuously** over a range of **loudness** and **frequency**.

Digital Signals Are Resistant to the Effects of Noise

When you **transmit** an electronic signal it will pick up **noise** (interference) from **electrical disturbances** or other **signals**. The receiver needs to be able to **reconstruct** the **original signal** from the **noisy signal** if they're to get an **accurate representation** of what was sent. This is **much easier** with **digital** than analogue signals because the **number of values** a digital signal can take is **limited**.

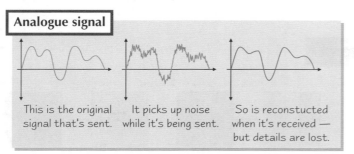

Analogue signal

This is the original signal that's sent. It picks up noise while it's being sent. So is reconstucted when it's received — but details are lost.

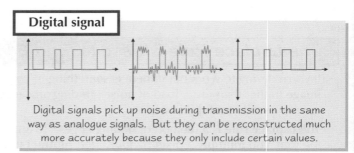

Digital signal

Digital signals pick up noise during transmission in the same way as analogue signals. But they can be reconstructed much more accurately because they only include certain values.

Analogue Signals can be Digitised

1) It's possible to turn an **analogue signal** into a **digital signal** — this is called **digitising** the signal.

2) To digitise a signal, you take the **value** of the signal at **regular time intervals**, then find the **nearest digital value**.

3) Each **digital value** is represented by a **binary number**, so you can **convert** the **analogue** values to **binary** numbers.

4) The **digital signal** you end up with won't be **exactly** the same as the **analogue signal**, but it's usually quite **close**.

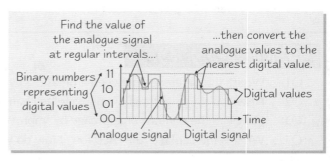

Find the value of the analogue signal at regular intervals... ...then convert the analogue values to the nearest digital value.

Binary numbers representing digital values { 11, 10, 01, 00

Digital values

Time

Analogue signal Digital signal

The Quality of a Digitised Signal Depends on Its Resolution

1) How well a **digitised** signal matches the original depends on **two** factors — the **difference** between the possible **digital values** (**resolution**) and the **time** from one **sample** to the next (**sampling rate**, see p13).

2) If a signal is digitised using only a **few, widely spaced** digital values, it's likely that a lot of the analogue values sampled will be **far** from the **nearest digital value**. But, if a **large** number of **closely spaced** digital values are used, most of the analogue values will be **very close** to a digital value, so will only change **slightly**.

3) This means that the **higher the resolution** (i.e. the **more possible digital values** there are), the **more closely** the digitised signal will **match** the original.

4) **Resolution** is determined by the **number of bits** in the **binary numbers** representing the digital values — the **greater** the number of **bits**, the **greater** the **resolution**.

5) When **music** is digitised to make **CDs** a resolution of **16 bits** is used. This gives a total of **65 536 digital values** and means the recorded music is **very similar** to the **original**.

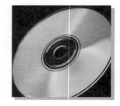

Sampling

Noise Limits the Number of Bits used for Sampling

You've just seen that the **higher the resolution**, the **better** a digitised signal **matches** the original. But, if the original signal contains **noise** (as most real signals do), then a really **fine resolution** will reproduce all the little wiggles caused by the **noise** — **not useful**. In practice, the **resolution** is **limited** by the **ratio** of the total **variation** in the **signal** to the **variation** caused by **noise**:

$$\textbf{Maximum number of bits} = \log_2\left(\frac{\textbf{Total variation}}{\textbf{Noise variation}}\right) \quad \text{or} \quad b = \log_2\left(\frac{V_{total}}{V_{noise}}\right)$$

Here the variation is measured in volts, but the ratio has no units because they cancel.

Minimum Sampling Rate is Twice the Maximum Frequency

1) When you **digitise** a signal, you **record the value** of (**sample**) the original signal at **regular intervals**. The **rate** at which you **sample** the signal is called the **sampling rate** — imaginative name, I know.

2) The **sampling rate** has to be **high** enough to record all the **high frequency** detail of the signal. The diagram on the **right** shows how **detail** can be **lost** if the sampling rate is too **low**.

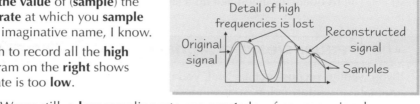

3) Worse still, a **low** sampling rate can **create** low frequency signals — called **aliases** — that **weren't** in the original signal at all. The diagram on the **left** shows how **aliases** can be **created** by a **low sampling rate**.

4) To avoid these problems, the **sampling rate** must be at least **twice** the **highest frequency** in the original signal.

Original signal — Samples — The reconstructed signal has a lower frequency than the original

$$\boxed{\textbf{Minimum rate of sampling} = 2 \times \textbf{maximum frequency of signal}}$$

Digital Signals Have Four Main Advantages Over Analogue Signals

1) Digital signals can be **sent**, **received** and **reproduced** more easily than analogue signals because they can only take a limited number of values.

2) Digital signals are **resistant** to the effects of **noise** — **analogue signals** are **negatively affected** by **noise**.

3) Digital signals can be used to represent **different** kinds of **information** in the **same way** — for example, **images** and **sounds** can both be represented as a string of bits.

4) Digital signals are **easy to process** using **computers**, since computers are **digital devices** too.

But, digital signals can **never** reproduce analogue signals **exactly** — some **information** will always be **lost**.

Practice Questions

Q1 Explain how a digital signal is different from an analogue one.

Q2 What is meant by resolution in the context of digitising analogue signals?

Q3 Describe two problems that can be caused by an insufficient sampling rate.

Q4 Give four advantages of digital signals over analogue.

Exam Questions

Q1 A digital signal has a total variation of 160 mV and a noise variation of 10 mV.
What is the maximum number of bits that should be used when sampling this signal? [2 marks]

Q2 An analogue signal contains frequencies at 100 Hz, 500 Hz, 310 Hz and 250 Hz.
What is the minimum sampling rate that should be used when digitising this signal? [1 mark]

How do finger puppets communicate? With digital signals...

Digital signals are everywhere these days — CDs, MP3s, DVDs, digital TV — there's just no escape. Analogue signals are still around, though — some people prefer them for listening to music and use vinyl (ask your dad) instead of CDs.

Signal Spectra and Bandwidth

I'm very sorry about the 'joke' on the previous page — the person responsible has been summoned to a meeting of the International Humour Committee to explain themself. For the rest of us, it's back to the wonderful world of signals...

Signals are Made Up of Lots of Different Frequencies

1) If you were asked to draw a **wave**, you'd probably sketch a **sine curve** (like the one on page 4). This is the **simplest** kind of **signal** because it contains just **one frequency**.

2) In practice, most **signals** are made up of **several** sine curves, all with **different frequencies**, added together. For example, if you play a **musical note**, the sound you hear contains the **frequency** (pitch) of the **main note** and a load of **other frequencies**. It's these '**other frequencies**' that make instruments **sound different**, even though they're playing the **same note**.

3) The **frequencies** that **make up** a **signal** are called its **spectrum**.

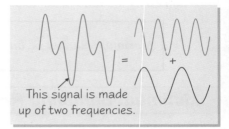
This signal is made up of two frequencies.

The Frequencies in a Signal Contain Information

If you want to **reconstruct** a signal, you need to know about **all** of the **frequencies** within it. All the frequencies in a signal carry **information**, so if you **lose** any of the frequencies, you **won't** get all the **information** from the signal. This is why the **sampling rate** (see page 13) is so important when **digitising** analogue signals.

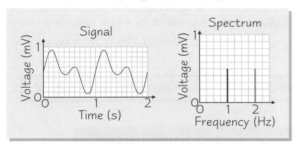

You can get information about the **frequencies** within a **signal** by **drawing** a graph of its **spectrum**. The graph shows the **amplitude** and **frequency** of **all** the waves that make up the signal.

The signal shown on the **left** is the same as the one **above**. The **two peaks** on the **spectrum** correspond to the **two frequencies** that make up the signal.

Most **signals** are made up of **several** frequencies with different amplitudes — their **spectra** would have **more**, **different sized peaks**.

Bandwidth is the Range of Frequencies within a Signal

You've just seen that a signal's **spectrum** is all the **frequencies** within the signal. The **range** that a **signal's spectrum** covers is called its **bandwidth**. You can find a signal's **bandwidth** by **subtracting** the **lowest frequency** within it from the **highest frequency** — or by looking at the **graph** of its **spectrum**.

The **bandwidth** of the **signal** in the examples above is: 2 Hz – 1 Hz = **1 Hz**.

In **communications** systems the **bandwidth** of each signal determines **how many** signals can be sent at the **same time** (see page 15 for an explanation).

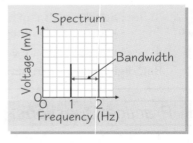

Communication Signals Are Transmitted Using Carrier Waves

1) When you **tune** a **radio** you scan through the **frequencies** it's receiving until you find the one you want. What you are searching for is the **frequency** of the **carrier wave** that **transmits** the signal from your station.

2) At the radio station, the **audio signal** from the presenter or music is converted to an **electronic signal**. This **signal** is then mixed with a **carrier wave**, and the combined signal is **transmitted**.

3) When your **radio** is tuned to the **right frequency**, it **receives** the **signal** from the radio station. It is able to **separate** the **actual signal** from the **carrier wave** and then convert this back into **sound** for you to listen to.

4) All **radio stations** are given a particular **carrier frequency** to broadcast their signal on. The **carrier frequencies** of all the stations in a local area have to be **different** so that they don't **interfere** with each other.

5) It's **not** just radio that uses this system — for example, **television** and **mobile telephone signals** are sent in the **same** way. The difference is that the **carrier frequencies** used for each system lie in **different parts** of the **electromagnetic spectrum**.

Signal Spectra and Bandwidth

Bandwidth Limits the Number of Signals that can be Transmitted

1) You've just seen that **radio stations** have to use **different** carrier frequencies so they don't **interfere** with each other. But there also has to be a **gap** between the **frequencies** used — for example, if 'Little FM' broadcasts with a frequency of 107.3 MHz, you **won't** find another station at 107.2 MHz or 107.4 MHz.

2) The **size** of the **gap** between frequencies is determined by the **bandwidth** of the **audio signal** — the **larger** the **bandwidth**, the **larger** the **gap** must be to **stop** signals at neighbouring carrier frequencies **overlapping**.

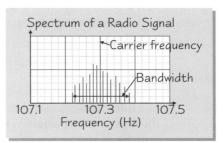

3) In practice, the **carrier frequencies** for radio stations are always **at least** 0.2 MHz apart and the signals are **filtered** (very high or low frequencies are removed) to make sure they **don't** exceed this range.

4) The **problem** with having gaps between the carrier frequencies is that it **limits** the **number of signals** that can be transmitted. For example, **FM radio** can be transmitted between **30 MHz and 300 MHz**. So with a gap of 0.2 MHz, there's **only** space for (300 − 30) ÷ 0.2 = **1350 stations**.

Rate of Transmission = Samples per Second × Bits per Sample

By now you should know **how** signals are **transmitted** — what's also important is the **rate** at which they're transmitted. The **rate of transmission** of a digital signal depends on **two** factors:

1) The number of **samples per second** — this must be at least **twice** the **highest frequency** in the signal to ensure that all the frequencies within its spectrum are transmitted accurately.

2) The number of **bits per sample** — this must be **high enough** that the transmitted signal **closely** matches the original, but not so high that it is negatively affected by **noise**.

Rate of transmission of a digital signal (bits per second) = **samples per second × bits per sample**

Practice Questions

Q1 What is meant by a) the spectrum and b) the bandwidth of a signal?

Q2 What are carrier signals used for?

Q3 Why is the number of signals that can be transmitted at the same time limited?

Exam Questions

Q1 The telephone system samples your voice 8000 times a second and converts this into an eight bit digital signal.

(a) What is the rate of transmission for bits in this telephone system? [1 mark]

(b) How many bytes are sent each second? [1 mark]

Q2 The diagram shows the spectrum of a signal.

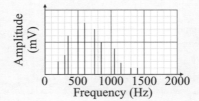

(a) What does the spectrum of a signal show? [1 mark]

(b) What is the bandwidth of this signal? [1 mark]

Bandwidth — the diameter of the drum kit...

Congratulations — you've made it through the pages on signalling. I don't know about you, but I think I'm going to celebrate with a nice cup of tea and a biscuit. Oh, wait, I should probably write up the answers to those pesky exam questions first.

Charge, Current and Potential Difference

This section isn't about the sixth sense, common sense or extrasensory perception.
It's about proper, sensible physics... such as how microphones are like ears...

Many **Sensors** are **Powered** using **Electricity**

Your body is pretty amazing at sensing things, within limits.
E.g. skin is a good temperature sensor — you know about it when you spill hot tea on
your lap — but you won't know that the temperature of the tea is 62.3 °C.

1) **Electronic sensors** are designed to sense things we can't (or we're too lazy to)
    sense. Any change in whatever the sensor's detecting will change the current
    in the connected circuit. The **current** is processed to give you a reading.

2) There are loads of different types of sensor out there. From everyday things
    like **microphones** that sense sound waves, to temperature sensors like
    thermistors, and **electron microscopes** which can be used to 'see'
    individual atoms (see p 31). Excited yet? I know I am...

*Debbie knew she was hotter
than Chantelle — they were
just waiting for the thermistor
to confirm it.*

Current is the **Rate** of **Flow** of **Charge**

The **current** in a **wire** is like **water** flowing in a **pipe**. The **amount** of water that flows depends on the
flow rate and the **time**. It's the same with electricity — **current is the rate of flow of charge**.

$$\Delta Q = I\Delta t \quad \text{or} \quad I = \frac{\Delta Q}{\Delta t}$$

Where ΔQ is the charge in coulombs,
I is the current and Δt is the time taken.

*Remember that conventional current flows from
+ to -, the opposite way from electron flow.*

The **Coulomb** is the **Unit** of Charge
One **coulomb** (**C**) is defined as the **amount of charge**
that passes in **1 second** when the **current** is **1 ampere**.

You can measure the current flowing through a part of a circuit using an **ammeter**.
Remember — you always need to attach an ammeter in **series** (so that the current
through the ammeter is the same as the current through the component — see page 22).

Potential Difference is the **Energy** per **Unit Charge**

To make electric charge flow through a component, you need to do
work on it. **Potential difference** (p.d.), or **voltage**, is defined as the
energy converted per unit charge moved.

$$V = \frac{W}{Q}$$

*W is the energy in joules. It's the
work you do moving the charge.*

Back to the 'water analogy' again.
The p.d. is like the pressure that's
forcing water along the pipe.

Resistor

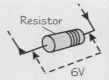

6V

Here you do 6 J of work moving each coulomb of charge
through the resistor, so the p.d. across it is 6 V.
The energy gets converted to heat.

Definition of the **Volt**
The **potential difference** across a component is **1 volt** when you convert
1 joule of energy moving **1 coulomb** of charge through the component.

$$1\,V = 1\,J\,C^{-1}$$

Charge, Current and Potential Difference

Power is the Rate of Transfer of Energy

Power (**P**) is **defined** as the **rate** of **transfer** of **energy** (the rate of work done). It's measured in **watts** (**W**), where **1 watt** is equivalent to **1 joule per second**.

or $$P = \frac{W}{t}$$

There's a really simple formula for **power** in **electrical circuits**:

$$P = IV$$

This makes sense, since:

1) **Potential difference** (**V**) is defined as the **energy transferred** per **coulomb**.
2) **Current** (**I**) is defined as the **number** of **coulombs** transferred per **second**.
3) So **p.d.** × **current** is **energy transferred per second**, i.e. **power**.

By rearranging the equation and substituting into the potential difference equation you can see that:

$$V = \frac{P}{I} = \frac{W}{Q}$$

P = W/t, I = Q/t, so time cancels.

Energy is Easy to Calculate if you Know the Power

Sometimes it's the **total energy** transferred (**the total work done**) that you're interested in. In this case you simply need to **multiply** the **power** by the **time**.

W = Pt, so $$W = VIt$$

Example

A prancing electro-monkey is powered by a 6 V battery and draws a current of 0.8 A. How much energy would the electro-monkey transfer if switched on and left to prance for 1 minute.

V = 6 V, **I** = 0.8 A, **t** = 60 seconds. So, **W = VIt** = 6 × 0.8 × 60 = <u>288 J</u>

Practice Questions

Q1 Describe in words how current and charge are related.
Q2 Define the coulomb.
Q3 Define potential difference.
Q4 Power is measured in watts. What is 1 watt equivalent to?

Exam Questions

Q1 A battery delivers 4500 C of electric charge to a circuit in 10 minutes. Calculate the average current. [2 marks]

Q2 A 12 V car battery supplies a current of 48 A for 2 seconds to the car's starter motor. Calculate the energy transferred from the battery. [1 mark]

Q3 An electric motor runs off a 12 V d.c. supply and has an overall efficiency of 75%. Calculate how much electric charge will pass through the motor when it does 90 J of work. [3 marks]

[THIS JOKE HAS BEEN CENSORED]... it was a good one as well...

OK, this is a good one, I saw this bottle of wine the other day called 'raisin d'être' — 'raison d'être' of course meaning 'reason for living', but spelled slightly different to make 'raisin', meaning 'grape'. Ho ho. Chuckled all the way out of Tesco.

Resistance and Conductance

Resistance is what causes components to heat up. When you get a load of components in a small area like a computer chip, that's a lot of heat. That's why even though you might be sweating buckets in your classroom learning about this stuff, computers get a nice air-conditioned room to help them keep cool.

Everything has Resistance

1) If you put a **potential difference** (p.d.) across an **electrical component**, a **current** will flow.

2) **How much** current you get for a particular **p.d.** depends on the **resistance** of the component.

3) You can think of a component's **resistance** as a **measure** of how **difficult** it is to get a **current** to **flow** through it.

Mathematically, **resistance** is: $$R = \frac{V}{I}$$

This equation **defines** resistance.

You also need to know the formula for the **inverse** of resistance — **conductance, G**.

$$G = \frac{I}{V}$$

This is a measure of how good an electrical conductor a component is. It's measured in Ω^{-1} or siemens, S.

4) **Resistance** is measured in **ohms** (Ω).

A component has a resistance of **1 Ω** if a **potential difference** of **1 V** makes a **current** of **1 A** flow through it.

5) Not only is the equation that defines resistance beautiful (OK, maybe not...), it also gives you a whole new way of calculating electrical power if you substitute it into **P = IV**.

$V = IR$, so $$P = IV = I^2R$$

6) This power is the rate that a component converts electrical energy into other types of energy, e.g. heat. This is known as **power dissipation**. In computers, power dissipation is a pain as you've got to try to keep the densely packed circuits cool. Much of the time though it's really useful — it's what makes light bulbs shine and electric heaters warm your toes.

I/V Graphs Show how Resistance Varies

The term '**I/V characteristic**' refers to a **graph** which shows how the **current** (**I**) flowing through a **component changes** as the **potential difference** (**V**) across it is increased.

The **shallower** the **gradient** of a characteristic **I/V** graph, the **greater** the **resistance** of the component.

A **curve** shows that the resistance is **changing**.

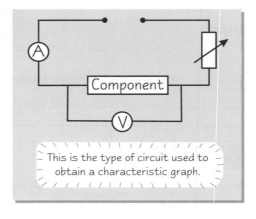

This is the type of circuit used to obtain a characteristic graph.

For an Ohmic Conductor, R is a Constant

A chap called **Ohm** did most of the early work on resistance. He developed a rule to **predict** how the **current** would **change** as the applied **potential difference increased**, for **certain types** of conductor. The rule is now called **Ohm's law** and the conductors that **obey** it (mostly metals) are called **ohmic conductors**.

Provided the **temperature** is **constant**, the **current** through an ohmic conductor is **directly proportional** to the **potential difference** across it.

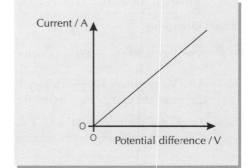

1) As you can see from the graph, **doubling** the **p.d. doubles** the **current**.

2) What this means is that the **resistance** is **constant**.

3) Often **factors** such as **light level** or **temperature** will have a **significant effect** on resistance (the resistivity changes), so you need to remember that Ohm's law is **only** true for **ohmic conductors** at **constant temperature**.

Resistance and Conductance

The I/V graph for a Filament Lamp is Curved

The characteristic graph for a **filament lamp** is a **curve**, which starts **steep** but gets **shallower** as the **voltage rises**. The **filament** in a lamp is just a **coiled up** length of **metal wire**, so you might think it should have the **same characteristic graph** as a **metallic conductor**. It doesn't because it **gets hot**. **Current** flowing through the lamp **increases** its **temperature**.

The **resistance** of a **metal increases** as the **temperature increases**.

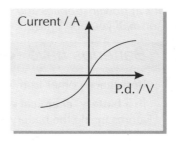

The Resistance of a Thermistor Depends on Temperature

1) A **thermistor** is a **resistor** with a **resistance** that depends on its **temperature** — so you can use them as **temperature sensors**. For the thermistor below, as the **temperature goes up**, its **resistance decreases**. The characteristic graph for this thermistor curves upwards.

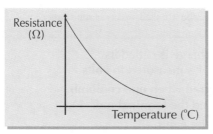

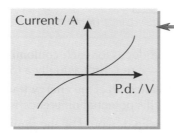

Increasing the current through the thermistor increases its temperature. The increasing gradient of this characteristic graph tells you that the resistance is decreasing

Warming the thermistor gives more **electrons** enough **energy** to **escape** from their atoms. This means that there are **more charge carriers** available, so the resistance is lower.

2) The **sensitivity** of **any** sensor is the **change** in the **output value measured** for a **given change** in the **input variable**.

$$\text{Sensitivity} = \frac{\text{change in dependent variable}}{\text{change in independent variable}}$$

3) So a thermistor's sensitivity is how much its resistance changes compared to the temperature change — which is the same as the **gradient** of the resistance-temperature graph.

Practice Questions

Q1 Name one environmental factor likely to alter the resistance of a component.

Q2 What is special about an ohmic conductor?

Exam Questions

Q1 The graph shows how the resistance of a light-dependent resistor (LDR) varies with light intensity. Describe how the sensitivity of the LDR varies with light intensity. [3 marks]

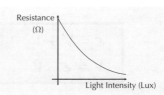

Q2 The table below shows some measurements taken by a student during an experiment investigating an unknown electrical component.

Potential Difference (V)	Current (mA)
2.0	2.67
7.0	9.33
11.0	14.67

(a) Use the first row of the table to calculate the resistance of the component when a p.d. of 2 V is applied. [2 marks]

(b) By means of further calculation, or otherwise, decide whether the component is an ohmic conductor. [3 marks]

I'm not a cry baby — I'm just sensitive...

It's really hard to resist a resistor joke (ir-resistor-ble in fact... ho ho). The examiners like testing this kind of stuff as if you've really done the experiment, so your results aren't perfect and you have errors fun to deal with. If errors aren't your thing (they sure fill me with fear...), have a quick flick to page 74 to calm your nerves.

E.m.f. and Internal Resistance

There's resistance everywhere — not just in filament lamps and those mysterious blocks called 'resistors'.
It's in power supplies and batteries, wires... pretty much anything you put in an electric circuit. Often the resistance is
so small you don't have to worry about it, but sometimes it's just too big to ignore.

Batteries have **Resistance**

From now on, I'm assuming that the resistance of the wires in the circuit is zero. In practice, they do have a small resistance.

Resistance comes from **electrons colliding** with **atoms** and **losing energy**.

In a **battery**, **chemical energy** is used to make **electrons move**. As they move, they collide with atoms inside the battery — so batteries **must** have resistance. This is called **internal resistance**.

Internal resistance is what makes **batteries** and **cells warm up** when they're used.

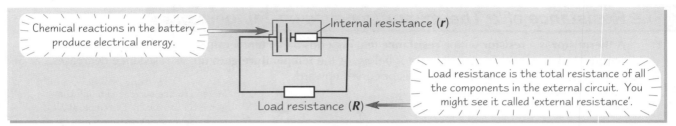

Chemical reactions in the battery produce electrical energy.

Internal resistance (**r**)

Load resistance is the total resistance of all the components in the external circuit. You might see it called 'external resistance'.

Load resistance (**R**)

1) The amount of **electrical energy** the battery produces for each **coulomb** of charge is called its **electromotive force** or e.m.f. (ε). Be careful — e.m.f. **isn't** actually a force. It's measured in **volts**.

2) The **potential difference** across the **load resistance** (**R**) is the **energy transferred** when **one coulomb** of charge flows through the **load resistance**. This potential difference is called the **terminal p.d.** (**V**).

3) If there was **no internal resistance**, the **terminal p.d.** would be the **same** as the **e.m.f.** However, in **real** power supplies, there's **always some energy lost** overcoming the internal resistance.

4) The **energy wasted per coulomb** overcoming the internal resistance is called the **lost volts** (**v**).

Conservation of energy tells us:

energy per coulomb supplied by the source	=	energy per coulomb used in load resistance	+	energy per coulomb wasted in internal resistance

There are Loads of **Calculations** with **E.m.f.** and **Internal Resistance**

Examiners can ask you to do **calculations** with **e.m.f.** and **internal resistance** in loads of **different** ways. You've got to be ready for whatever they throw at you.

$$\varepsilon = V + v \qquad \varepsilon = I(R + r)$$
$$V = \varepsilon - v \qquad V = \varepsilon - Ir$$

Learn these equations for the exam. Only this one will be on your formula sheet.

These are all basically the **same equation**, just written differently. If you're given enough information you can calculate the e.m.f. (ε), terminal p.d. (**V**), lost volts (**v**), current (**I**), load resistance (**R**) or internal resistance (**r**). Which equation you should use depends on what information you've got, and what you need to calculate.

Most Power Supplies Need Low Internal Resistance

A **car battery** has to deliver a **really high current** — so it needs to have a **low internal resistance**. **Generally**, batteries have an **internal resistance** of **less than 1 Ω**.

Since **internal resistance** causes **energy loss**, you'd think **all** power supplies should have a **low internal resistance**.

High voltage power supplies are the **exception**. **HT** (high tension) and **EHT** (extremely high tension) **supplies** are designed with **very high** internal resistances. This means that if they're **accidentally short-circuited** only a **very small current** can flow. Much **safer**.

E.m.f. and Internal Resistance

Use this **Circuit** to **Measure Internal Resistance** and **E.m.f.**

By **changing** the value of **R** (**load resistance**) in this circuit and **measuring** the **current** (**I**) and **p.d.** (**V**), you can work out the **internal resistance** of the source.

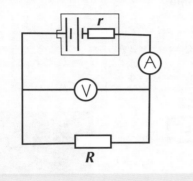

Start with the equation:

$$V = \varepsilon - Ir$$

Plot a graph of **V** against **I**.

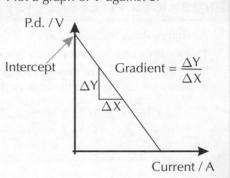

1) Rearrange the equation: $V = -rI + \varepsilon$
2) Since ε and r are constants, that's just the equation of a **straight line** (in the form: $y = \mathbf{m}x + \mathbf{c}$).
3) So the intercept on the vertical axis is ε.
4) And the gradient is $-r$.

Equation of a straight line
$$y = \mathbf{m}x + \mathbf{c}$$
gradient   y-intercept

An **easier** way to **measure** the **e.m.f.** of a **power source** is by connecting a high-resistance **voltmeter** across its **terminals**. A **small current flows** through the **voltmeter**, so there must be some **lost volts** — this means you measure a value **very slightly less** than the **e.m.f.** In **practice** the difference **isn't** usually **significant**.

Practice Questions

Q1 What causes internal resistance?

Q2 What is meant by 'lost volts'?

Q3 What is the difference between e.m.f. and terminal p.d.?

Q4 Write the equation used to calculate the terminal p.d. of a power supply.

Exam Questions

Q1 A large battery with an internal resistance of 0.8 Ω and e.m.f. 24 V is used to power a dentist's drill with resistance 4 Ω.

(a) Calculate the current in the circuit when the drill is connected to the power supply.   [2 marks]

(b) Calculate the voltage across the drill while it is being used.   [1 mark]

Q2 A student mistakenly connects a 10 Ω ray box to an HT power supply of 500 V.
The ray box does not light, and the student measures the current flowing to be only 50 mA.

(a) Calculate the internal resistance of the HT power supply.   [2 marks]

(b) Explain why this is a sensible internal resistance for an HT power supply.   [2 marks]

You're UNBELIEVABLE... [Frantic air guitar]... Ueuuurrrrghhh... Yeah...

Wanting power supplies to have a low internal resistance makes sense, you wouldn't want your MP3 player battery melting if you listened to music for more than half an hour. Make sure you know your e.m.f. equations, they're an exam fave. A good way to get them learnt is to keep trying to get from one equation to another... dull, but it can help.

Conservation of Energy & Charge in Circuits

Prepare to be shocked: real-life computer circuits are more complicated than the ones you set up in lab lessons. Fact. But it's always the same principle. Microchips are a maze of electronic components that all need to have certain amounts of current flowing through them, some at the same time. That's where parallel and series circuits come in...

Charge Doesn't 'Leak Away' Anywhere — it's Conserved

1) As **charge flows** through a circuit, it **doesn't** get **used up** or **lost**.
2) This means that whatever **charge flows into** a junction will **flow out** again.
3) Since **current** is **rate of flow of charge**, it follows that whatever **current flows into** a junction is the same as the current **flowing out** of it.

e.g.

> *CHARGE FLOWING IN 1 SECOND*
> $Q_1 = 6\,C \Rightarrow I_1 = 6\,A$ ⟶
> $Q_2 = 2\,C \Rightarrow I_2 = 2\,A$
> $Q_3 = 4\,C \Rightarrow I_3 = 4\,A$
> $I_1 = I_2 + I_3$

> The total **current entering a junction** = the total **current leaving it**.

Energy conservation is vital.

Energy is Conserved too

1) **Energy is conserved.** You already know that. In **electrical circuits**, **energy** is **transferred round** the circuit. Energy **transferred to** a charge is **e.m.f.**, and energy **transferred from** a charge is **potential difference**.
2) In a **closed loop**, these two quantities must be **equal** if energy is conserved (which it is).

> The **total e.m.f.** around a **series circuit** = the **sum** of the **p.d.s** across each component. (or $\varepsilon = \Sigma IR$ in symbols)

Exam Questions get you to Apply Conservation Laws to Combinations of Resistors

A **typical exam question** will give you a **circuit** with bits of information missing, leaving you to fill in the gaps. Not the most fun... but on the plus side you get to ignore any internal resistance stuff (unless the question tells you otherwise)... hurrah. You need to remember the **following rules**:

SERIES Circuits

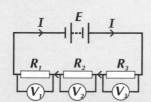

1) **same current** at **all points** of the circuit (since there are no junctions)
2) **e.m.f. split** between **components** so: $E = V_1 + V_2 + V_3$
3) $V = IR$, so if I is constant: $IR_{total} = IR_1 + IR_2 + IR_3$
4) cancelling the Is gives:

> $R_{total} = R_1 + R_2 + R_3$

PARALLEL Circuits

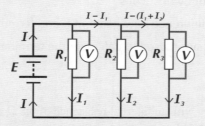

1) **current** is **split** at each **junction**, so: $I = I_1 + I_2 + I_3$
2) **same p.d.** across **all components** (three separate loops — within each loop the e.m.f. equals sum of individual p.d.s)
3) so, $V/R_{total} = V/R_1 + V/R_2 + V/R_3$
4) cancelling the Vs gives: $1/R_{total} = 1/R_1 + 1/R_2 + 1/R_3$
5) or $G = G_1 + G_2 + G_3$

...and there's an example on the next page to make sure you know what to do with all that...

Conservation of Energy & Charge in Circuits

Worked Exam Question

A battery of e.m.f. 16 V and negligible internal resistance is connected in a circuit as shown:

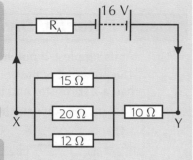

a)   Show that the group of resistors between X and Y could be replaced by a single resistor of resistance 15 Ω.

You can find the **combined resistance** of the 15 Ω, 20 Ω and 12 Ω resistors using:

$G = G_1 + G_2 + G_3$ = 1/15 + 1/20 + 1/12 = 1/5, $R = 1/G \Rightarrow R = 5$ Ω

So **overall resistance** between **X** and **Y** can be found by $R = R_1 + R_2 = 5 + 10 = 15$ Ω

b)   If $R_A = 20$ Ω:
   (i) calculate the potential difference across R_A,

Careful — there are a few steps here. You need the p.d. across R_A, but you don't know the current through it. So start there:
total resistance in circuit = 20 + 15 = 35 Ω, **so** current through R_A can be found using $I = V_{total}/R_{total}$:

$I = 16/35$ A

then you can use $V = IR_A$ to find the p.d. across R_A: $V = 16/35 \times 20 = $ **9.1 V**

   (ii) calculate the current in the 15 Ω resistor.

You know the **current flowing** into the group of three resistors and out of it, but not through the individual branches. But you know that their **combined resistance** is **5 Ω** (from part a) so you can work out the p.d. across the group:

$V = IR = 16/35 \times 5 = 16/7$ V

The p.d. across the **whole group** is the same as the p.d. across each **individual resistor**, so you can use this to find the current through the 15 Ω resistor:

$I = V/R = (16/7) / 15 = $ **0.15 A**

Practice Questions

Q1   Which two quantities must be equal in a closed loop circuit?

Q2   Find the current through and potential difference across each of two resistors, each with a conductance of 0.2 S, when they are placed in a circuit containing a 5 V battery, and are wired: a) in series, b) in parallel.

Exam Question

Q1   For the circuit on the right:

   (a) Calculate the total effective resistance of the three resistors in this combination.   [2 marks]

   (b) Calculate the main current, I_3.   [2 marks]

   (c) Calculate the potential difference across the 4 Ω resistor.   [1 mark]

   (d) Calculate the potential difference across the parallel pair of resistors.
   [1 mark]

   (e) Using your answer from 1 (d), calculate the currents I_1 and I_2.   [2 marks]

This is a very purple page — needs a bit of yellow I think...

V = IR is the formula you'll use most often in these questions. Make sure you know whether you're using it on the overall circuit, or just one specific component. It's amazingly easy to get muddled up — you've been warned.

The Potential Divider

Potential dividers are part of soooo many sensors. You use them to make light sensors (photoconductive sensors), displacement sensors, heat sensors and so much more. They tell you when your fuel's running low or if a burglar's in your house, and they can even let you crank up the volume when you're listening to Cliff on your stereo...

Use a **Potential Divider** to get a **Fraction** of a **Source Voltage**

1) At its simplest, a **potential divider** is a circuit with a **voltage source** and a couple of **resistors** in series.

2) The **potential** of the voltage source (e.g. a power supply) is **divided** in the **ratio** of the **resistances**. So, if you had a **2 Ω** resistor and a **3 Ω** resistor, you'd get **2/5** of the p.d. across the **2 Ω** resistor and **3/5** across the **3 Ω**.

3) That means you can **choose** the **resistances** to get the **voltage** you **want** across one of them.

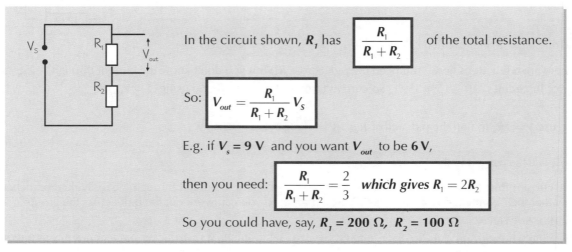

In the circuit shown, R_1 has $\dfrac{R_1}{R_1 + R_2}$ of the total resistance.

So: $$V_{out} = \frac{R_1}{R_1 + R_2} V_s$$

E.g. if $V_s = 9\,V$ and you want V_{out} to be **6 V**,

then you need: $\dfrac{R_1}{R_1 + R_2} = \dfrac{2}{3}$ *which gives* $R_1 = 2R_2$

So you could have, say, $R_1 = 200\,\Omega$, $R_2 = 100\,\Omega$

4) This circuit is mainly used for **calibrating voltmeters**, which have a **very high resistance**.

5) If you put something with a **relatively low resistance** across R_1 though, you start to run into **problems**. You've **effectively** got **two resistors** in **parallel**, which will **always** have a **total** resistance **less** than R_1. That means that V_{out} will be **less** than you've calculated, and will depend on what's connected across R_1. Hrrumph.

Add an **LDR** or **Thermistor** for a **Light** or **Temperature Switch**

1) A **light-dependent resistor** (LDR) has a very **high resistance** in the **dark**, but a **lower resistance** in the **light**.

2) An **NTC thermistor** has a **high resistance** at **low temperatures**, but a much **lower resistance** at **high temperatures** (it varies in the opposite way to a normal resistor, only much more so).

3) Either of these can be used as one of the **resistors** in a **potential divider**, giving an **output voltage** that **varies** with the **light level** or **temperature**.

4) Add a **transistor** and you've got yourself a **switch**, e.g. to turn on a light or a heating system.

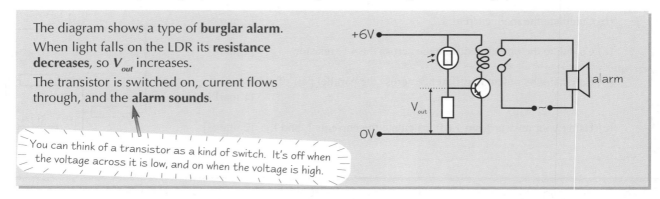

The diagram shows a type of **burglar alarm**.
When light falls on the LDR its **resistance decreases**, so V_{out} increases.
The transistor is switched on, current flows through, and the **alarm sounds**.

You can think of a transistor as a kind of switch. It's off when the voltage across it is low, and on when the voltage is high.

The Potential Divider

A *Potentiometer* uses a *Variable Resistor* to give a *Variable Voltage*

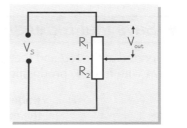

1) A **potentiometer** has a variable resistor replacing R_1 and R_2 of the potential divider, but it uses the **same idea** (it's even sometimes **called** a potential divider just to confuse things).

2) You move a **slider** or turn a knob to **adjust** the **relative sizes** of R_1 and R_2. That way you can vary V_{out} from **0 V** up to the source voltage.

3) This is dead handy when you want to be able to **change** a **voltage continuously**, like in the **volume control** of a stereo.

Here, V_s is replaced by the input signal (e.g. from a CD player) and V_{out} is the output to the amplifier and loudspeaker.

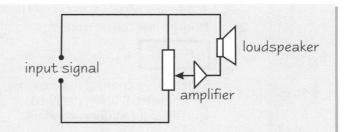

Practice Questions

Q1 Look at the burglar alarm circuit on page 24. How could you change the circuit so that the alarm sounds when the light level decreases?

Q2 The LDR in the burglar alarm circuit has a resistance of $300\,\Omega$ when light and $900\,\Omega$ when dark. The fixed resistor has a value of $100\,\Omega$. Show that V_{out} (light) = 1.5 V and V_{out} (dark) = 0.6 V.

Exam Questions

Q1 In the circuit on the right, all the resistors have the same value. Calculate the p.d. between:

    (i)   A and B.   [1 mark]

    (ii)   A and C.   [1 mark]

    (iii) B and C.   [1 mark]

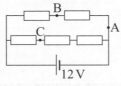

Q2 Look at the circuit on the right.

    (a)   Calculate the p.d. between A and B as shown by a high resistance voltmeter placed between the two points.   [1 mark]

    (b)   A $40\,\Omega$ resistor is now placed between points A and B. Calculate the p.d. across AB and the current flowing through the $40\,\Omega$ resistor.   [4 marks]

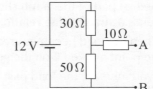

OI...YOU... [bang bang bang]... turn that potentiometer down...

You'll probably have to use a potentiometer in every experiment you do with electricity from now on in, so you'd better get used to them. I can't stand the things myself, but then lab and me don't mix — far too technical.

Hooke's Law

You don't want to make a lion cage out of polystyrene, and you need to know the material you build a skyscraper with will be able to take the weight of more than three people. You need to know what properties your material should have, and then do some testing to find out which ones have them. Welcome to the world of stress, strain and Hooke's law...

Hooke's Law Says that Extension is Proportional to Force

If a **metal wire** is supported at the top and then a weight attached to the bottom, it **stretches**.
The weight pulls down with force **F**, producing an equal and opposite force at the support.

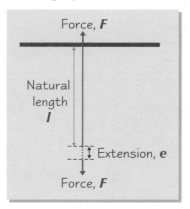

Force, **F**

Natural length **l**

Extension, **e**

Force, **F**

1) **Robert Hooke** discovered in 1676 that the extension of a stretched wire, **e**, is proportional to the load or force, **F**. This relationship is now called **Hooke's law**.

2) Hooke's law can be written:

$$F = ke$$

Where **k** is a constant that depends on the material being stretched. **k** is called the **stiffness constant**.

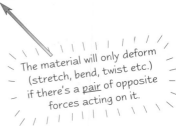

The material will only deform (stretch, bend, twist etc.) if there's a pair of opposite forces acting on it.

I'm a bit irrelevant on this page — bungee ropes don't obey Hooke's Law... Do you think I need to get out more?

Hooke's law Also Applies to Springs

A metal spring also changes length when you apply a **pair of opposite forces**.

1) The **extension** or **compression** of a spring is **proportional** to the **force** applied — so Hooke's law applies.

2) For springs, **k** in the formula **F = ke** is usually called the **spring stiffness** or **spring constant**.

> Hooke's law works just as well for **compressive** forces as **tensile** forces. For a spring, **k** has the **same value** whether the forces are tensile or compressive (that's not true for all materials).

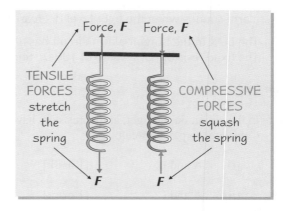

Force, **F**   Force, **F**

TENSILE FORCES
stretch the spring

COMPRESSIVE FORCES
squash the spring

F   **F**

Hooke's law Stops Working when the Load is Great Enough

There's a **limit** to the force you can apply for Hooke's law to stay true.

1) The graph shows load against extension for a **typical metal wire**.

2) The first part of the graph shows Hooke's law being obeyed — there's a **straight-line relationship** between **load** and **extension**.

3) When the load becomes great enough, the graph starts to **curve**. The point marked E on the graph is called the **elastic limit**.

4) If you increase the load past the elastic limit, the material will be **permanently stretched**. When all the force is removed, the material will be **longer** than at the start.

5) **Metals** generally obey Hooke's law up to the limit of proportionality (see p 33), which is very near the elastic limit.

6) Be careful — there are some materials, like **rubber**, that only obey Hooke's law for **really small** extensions.

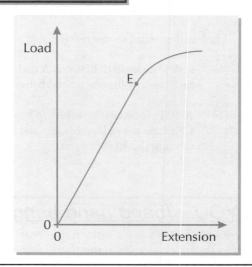

Load

E

0

0   Extension

Hooke's Law

So basically...

A Stretch can be Elastic or Plastic

Elastic

If a **deformation** is **elastic**, the material returns to its **original shape** once the forces are removed.

1) When the material is put under **tension**, the **atoms** of the material are **pulled apart** from one another.

2) Atoms can **move** small distances relative to their **equilibrium positions**, without actually changing position in the material.

3) Once the **load** is **removed**, the atoms **return** to their **equilibrium** distance apart.

For a metal, elastic deformation happens as long as **Hooke's law** is obeyed.

Plastic

If a deformation is **plastic**, the material is **permanently stretched**.

1) Some atoms in the material move position relative to one another.

2) When the load is removed, the **atoms don't return** to their original positions.

A metal stretched **past its elastic limit** shows plastic deformation.

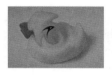

Donald wasn't keen on plastic deformation...

Practice Questions

Q1 State Hooke's law.

Q2 Define tensile forces and compressive forces.

Q3 Explain what is meant by the elastic limit of a material.

Q4 From studying the force-extension graph for a material as it is loaded and unloaded, how can you tell:
(a) if Hooke's law is being obeyed,
(b) if the elastic limit has been reached?

Q5 What is plastic behaviour of a material under load?

Exam Questions

Q1 A metal guitar string stretches 4.0 mm when a 10 N force is applied.

(a) If the string obeys Hooke's law, how far will the string stretch with a 15 N force? [1 mark]

(b) Calculate the stiffness constant for this string in Nm⁻¹. [2 marks]

(c) The string is tightened beyond its elastic limit. What would be noticed about the string? [1 mark]

Q2 A rubber band is 6.0 cm long. When it is loaded with 2.5 N, its length becomes 10.4 cm. Further loading increases the length to 16.2 cm when the force is 5.0 N.

Does the rubber band obey Hooke's law when the force on it is 5.0 N?
Justify your answer with a suitable calculation. [2 marks]

Sod's Law — if you don't learn it, it'll be in the exam...

Okay, so this isn't the most riveting stuff in the world — but at least it's fairly simple. I promise you, Physics does get more interesting than this. Wait till page 46 — you'll be longing for a bit of 17th century tedium then.

Stress, Strain and the Young Modulus

How much a material stretches for a particular applied force depends on its dimensions.
If you want to compare the properties of two different materials, you need to use stress and strain instead.
A stress-strain graph is the same for any sample of a particular material — the size of the sample doesn't matter.

A Stress Causes a Strain

A material subjected to a pair of **opposite forces** might **deform**, i.e. **change shape**. If the forces **stretch** the material, they're **tensile**. If the forces **squash** the material, they're **compressive**.

1) **Tensile stress** is defined as the **force applied**, *F*, divided by the **cross-sectional area**, *A*:

$$\text{stress} = \frac{F}{A}$$

The **units** of stress are **Nm⁻²** or pascals, **Pa**.

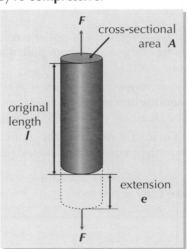

2) **Tensile strain** is defined as the **change in length**, i.e. the **extension**, divided by the **original length** of the material:

$$\text{strain} = \frac{e}{l}$$

Strain has **no units** — it's just a **number**.

3) It doesn't matter whether the forces producing the **stress** and **strain** are **tensile** or **compressive** — the **same equations** apply. The only difference is that you tend to think of **tensile** forces as **positive**, and **compressive** forces as **negative**.

A Stress Big Enough to Break the Material is Called the Breaking Stress

As a greater and greater tensile **force** is applied to a material, the **stress** on it **increases**.

1) The effect of the **stress** is to start to **pull** the **atoms apart** from one another.

2) Eventually the stress becomes **so great** that atoms **separate completely**, and the **material breaks**. This is shown by point **B** on the graph. The stress at which this occurs is called the **fracture stress**.

3) The point marked **UTS** on the graph is called the **ultimate tensile stress**. This is the **maximum stress** that the material can withstand.

4) **Engineers** have to consider the **UTS** and **fracture stress** of materials when designing a **structure**.

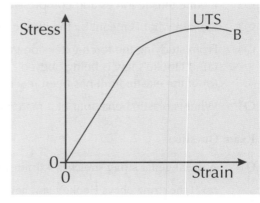

The Young Modulus is Stress ÷ Strain

When you apply a **load** to stretch a material, it experiences a **tensile stress** and a **tensile strain**.

1) Up to a point called the **limit of proportionality** (see p 33), the stress and strain of a material are proportional to each other.

2) So below this limit, for a particular material, stress divided by strain is a constant. This constant is called the **Young modulus**, *E*.

$$E = \frac{\text{tensile stress}}{\text{tensile strain}} = \frac{F/A}{e/l} = \frac{Fl}{eA}$$

Where, *F* = force in N, *A* = cross-sectional area in m²,
l = initial length in m and *e* = extension in m.

3) The **units** of the Young modulus are the same as stress (**Nm⁻²** or pascals), since strain has no units.

4) The Young modulus is used by **engineers** to make sure their materials can withstand sufficient forces.

Stress, Strain and the Young Modulus

To **Find** the Young Modulus, You need a **Very Long Wire**

This is the experiment you're most likely to do in class:

Mum moment: if you're doing this experiment, <u>wear safety goggles</u> — if the wire snaps, it could get very messy...

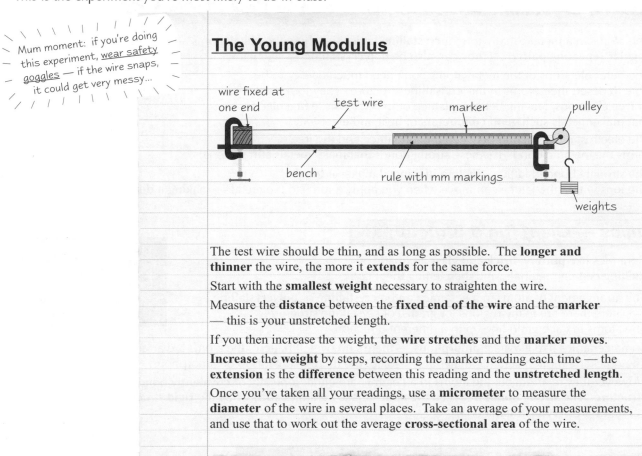

The Young Modulus

wire fixed at one end   test wire   marker   pulley

bench   rule with mm markings   weights

The test wire should be thin, and as long as possible. The **longer and thinner** the wire, the more it **extends** for the same force.

Start with the **smallest weight** necessary to straighten the wire.

Measure the **distance** between the **fixed end of the wire** and the **marker** — this is your unstretched length.

If you then increase the weight, the **wire stretches** and the **marker moves**.

Increase the **weight** by steps, recording the marker reading each time — the **extension** is the **difference** between this reading and the **unstretched length**.

Once you've taken all your readings, use a **micrometer** to measure the **diameter** of the wire in several places. Take an average of your measurements, and use that to work out the average **cross-sectional area** of the wire.

The other standard way of measuring the Young modulus in the lab is using **Searle's apparatus**. This is a bit more accurate, but it's harder to do and the equipment's more complicated.

Practice Questions

Q1   Write a definition for tensile stress and tensile strain.

Q2   What is meant by the fracture stress of a material?

Q3   Describe an experiment to find the Young Modulus of a material.

Exam Question

Q1   A steel wire is 2.00 m long. When a 300 N force is applied to the wire, it stretches 4.0 mm.
The wire has a circular cross-section with a diameter of 1.0 mm.

     (a)   What is the cross-sectional area of the wire?   [1 mark]

     (b)   Calculate the tensile stress in the wire.   [1 mark]

     (c)   Calculate the tensile strain of the wire.   [1 mark]

UTS a laugh a minute, this stuff...

Here endeth the proper physics for this section — the rest of it's materials science (and I don't care what your exam board says). It's all a bit "useful" for my liking. Calls itself a physics course... grumble... grumble... wasn't like this in my day... But to be fair — some of it's quite interesting, and there are some pretty pictures coming up...

Structures of Solids

The reason materials are flexible or tough is down to their structure.
When the going gets tough, the tough get going to page 32 to look up the definition of tough...

Metals — a Crystalline Structure with a 'Sea' of Free Electrons

1) The atoms in a metal usually form a **crystalline** lattice — where the metal atoms are arranged in a **regular repeating pattern**. (They can also be **polycrystalline** — see below).

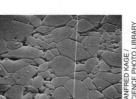

2) The outer electrons of the metal atoms don't need much energy to be able to desert their atoms in this crytsalline structure. They form a 'sea' of **free electrons,** leaving behind a lattice of ions. It's these free electrons that make metals such **good conductors** of heat and electricity.

3) The electrostatic attraction between the ion lattice and the free electrons forms the metallic bond. It's these **strong** bonds that make metals **stiff** materials.

4) The strongly bonded lattice structure of a metal makes it **tough**. The ions within the lattice can **move** when you apply a force to the metal — making it **ductile**.

Ceramics — Giant Rigid Structures

1) Ceramics like **pottery**, **brick** and **glass** are made by melting certain materials, and then letting them cool.

MANFRED KAGE / SCIENCE PHOTO LIBRARY

2) The arrangement of atoms in a ceramic can be **crystalline** or **polycrystalline** — where there are many regions (or **grains**) of crystalline structure. The atoms in each grain line up in a different direction.

3) Some ceramics like **glass** are **amorphous** — there's no overall pattern; the atoms are arranged at **random**. The quicker a molten ceramic material is cooled, the more likely it is to be amorphous.

4) However they're arranged, the atoms in a ceramic are either **ionically** or **covalently** bonded in a **giant rigid structure**. The **strong bonds** between the atoms make ceramics **stiff**, while the **rigid** structure means that ceramics are very **brittle** materials.

Polymers — Lots of Monomers Joined Together

1) A **polymer** is a molecular **chain**, made up of a **single repeating unit** called a **monomer**.

2) You get **natural** polymers like rubber, as well as a whole host of **man-made** ones like polythene.

3) The monomers in a polymer chain are **covalently** bonded together, and so are very hard to separate. This means even the thin polymer material used to make carrier bags is still pretty **strong**.

4) The polymer chains are often scrunched up or folded, and can unfold by **rotating** about their bonds when you pull them. This is what makes polymer materials **flexible**. The more easily the monomers can rotate, the more flexible the polymer will be.

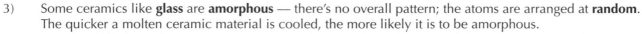

5) The strength and number of bonds **between** the chains also affect a polymer's flexibility. The stronger the cross-linking bonds, and the more cross-linking bonds you've got, the more **rigid** the material.

Composites — Combine the Properties of Different Materials

Composites are a bit like a pick 'n' mix — you combine two different materials to get a material with the properties you want.

One of the most common composites is **reinforced concrete**. Normal concrete is really **strong** when you try to **compress** it, but is **brittle** under any sort of **tension** force, like when being bent. Obviously if you're making a building out of concrete, using a brittle material wouldn't be too great an idea. To increase the strength of the concrete structure under tension, you embed **steel rods** into it. Ta da... reinforced concrete.

Structures of Solids

You Can Use **Electron Microscope Images** to **Estimate** the **Size** of **Atoms**

1) There are loads of different ways you can look at the structure of a material.

2) You can use powerful **optical microscopes** to get a good view of the surface of a material.

3) **Scanning Electron Microscopes** (SEM) and **Atomic Force Microscopes** (AFM) don't let you see a material's surface directly, but can be used to build up an atom-by-atom image of the surface on a computer screen.

4) You can use images like this to estimate and measure the size of the atoms in a material. Each 'blob' shows the size and position of an individual atom in the regular lattice. By knowing the width shown by the image, you can work out the width of an atom.

Example

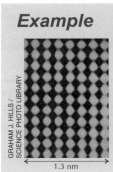

GRAHAM J. HILLS / SCIENCE PHOTO LIBRARY

1.3 nm

The figure shows a high-resolution transmission electron micrograph (HREM) image of a thin gold lattice. The field of view shown by this image is 1.3 nm. Estimate the typical size of a gold atom.

The width of this gold image is roughly 7 atoms and the width shown by the image is 1.3 nm — so you can find a rough size of a gold atom by dividing the width of the image by how many atoms it is across.

The distance from atom centre to atom centre = 1.3 ÷ 7 = **0.19 nm**.

5) Microscope images only ever show you the **surface** of a material — the structure underneath might be **completely different**. You need techniques like **X-ray crystallography** to really see how the atoms in a material are arranged.

Practice Questions

Q1 Describe the structure of a typical metal.

Q2 Describe the arrangement of atoms in an amorphous solid.

Q3 What is a polymer? Give one factor that affects how rigid a polymer material is.

Q4 Write down one technique that can show the atomic arrangement of a substance on its surface.

Exam Questions

Q1 Give one example of a composite material.
State an application for your chosen material.
Write down one advantage of using this composite material over a non-composite. [3 marks]

Q2 The figure shows a Scanning Tunnelling Microscope (STM) image of a layer of metal atoms.
The field of view shown by the height of the image is 4.05 nm.
Estimate the average size of the atoms shown.

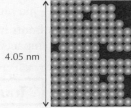

4.05 nm

[2 marks]

And that's why shops don't make their bags out of clay...

It's like what Trisha's been saying all along — it's what's on the inside that counts... and it's no different for bricks. Make sure you get to grips with the structure of each class of materials so you can explain why hard materials are hard, why floppy materials flop, and why it wouldn't be such a great idea to make a glass bungee cord...

Mechanical Properties of Solids

You wouldn't try doing surgery with scalpels made out of marshmallows, just as you wouldn't make a glass crash mat. It's important to know the mechanical properties of materials so you can select the best ones to suit your needs.

Terms to Describe the *Behaviour of Solids* Have *Precise Meanings*

Brittle materials break suddenly without deforming plastically.

If you apply a **force** to a **brittle material**, it won't **deform plastically** (see p 27), but will suddenly **snap** when the force gets to a certain size. Brittle materials can also be quite **weak** if they have **cracks** in them.

A **chocolate bar** is an example of a brittle material — you can break chunks of chocolate off the bar without the whole thing changing shape. **Ceramics** (e.g. **glass** and **pottery**) are brittle too — they tend to shatter.

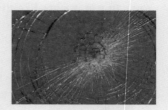

Ductile materials can be drawn into wires without losing their strength.

You can change the **shape** of **ductile materials** by drawing them into **wires** or other shapes. The important thing is that they **keep their strength** when they're deformed like this.

Copper is ductile, and with its high electrical conductivity this means that it's ideal for **electric wires**. A **ductile material** has been used for the cables supporting the **ski lift** in the photo — it's been drawn into long wires, but kept its strength.

Malleable materials change shape but may lose their strength.

The shape of **malleable materials** can be changed fairly easily, e.g. by **hammering** or **rolling**. The difference between malleable and ductile materials is that **malleable** materials **won't** necessarily **keep their strength**.

Gold is an example of a malleable metal — you can change the shape of a gold ring using just your fingers. **Brass** is malleable too — it can be bent and stretched into **complex shapes** to make musical instruments.

Hard materials are very resistant to cutting, indentation and abrasion.

If you try to cut, dent or scratch a hard material, you'll probably have very little effect. Their structure means **hard materials** are **resistant** to **cutting**, **indentation** (becoming dented) and **abrasion** (scratching).

Cutting tools (e.g. chisels) need to be harder than the stuff they're cutting — they're often made from **hardened steel**. **Diamond** is just about the hardest material there is — it's often used to reinforce the tips of drill bits.

Stiff materials have a high resistance to bending and stretching.

Changing the shape of **stiff materials** is really difficult as they are **resistant** to both **bending** and **stretching**. Stiffness is measured by the **Young modulus** (see p 28) — the higher the value, the stiffer the material.

The outer protective casing of **safety helmets** and **safety boots** need to be very stiff so that they keep their shape and don't **crush** onto your body when something impacts on them.

Tough materials are really difficult to break.

Toughness is a measure of the **energy** a material can **absorb** before it breaks. Really **tough materials** can absorb a lot of energy so are very **difficult** to **break**.

Some **polymers**, including certain types of **polythene**, are very tough. The hull of this **kayak** is made of a tough material so it won't break on rocks.

Mechanical Properties of Solids

Do you remember that lovely stress-strain graph from page 28? Well, it turns out that because different solids have different properties, their stress-strain graphs look different too.

Stress-Strain Graphs for Ductile Materials Curve

The diagram shows a **stress-strain graph** for a typical **ductile** material — e.g. a copper wire.

Point **Y** is the **yield point** — here the material suddenly starts to **stretch** without any extra load. The **yield point** (or yield stress) is the **stress** at which a large amount of **plastic deformation** takes place with a **constant** or **reduced load**.

Point **E** is the **elastic limit** — at this point the material starts to behave **plastically**. From point E onwards, the material would **no longer** return to its **original shape** once the stress was removed.

Point **P** is the **limit of proportionality** — after this, the graph is no longer a straight line but starts to **bend**. At this point, the material **stops** obeying **Hooke's law**, but would still **return** to its **original shape** if the stress was removed.

Before point **P**, the graph is a **straight line** through the **origin**. This shows that the material is obeying **Hooke's law** (page 26).

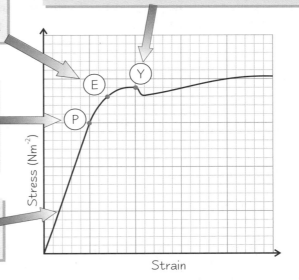

Brittle materials (e.g. glass, perspex, cast iron, chocolate chip cookies... mmmm... cookies) **don't** tend to behave plastically. They **fracture** before they reach the elastic limit.

Practice Questions

Q1 Write short definitions of the following terms: ductile, stiff, tough, brittle.

Q2 What is the difference between the limit of proportionality and the elastic limit?

Q3 Sketch stress-strain graphs of typical ductile material.

Q4 What property of a material is tested by finding the fracture stress needed to break a material?

Exam Questions

Q1 Hardened steel is a hard, brittle form of steel made by heating it up slowly and then quenching it in cold water.

(a) What is meant by the terms *hard* and *brittle*? [2 marks]

(b) Write down one application in which hardened steel could be used. Explain why it would be useful in this context. [2 marks]

(c) Sketch a stress-strain graph for hardened steel. [2 marks]

Q2 Riding helmets are designed to protect a rider's head from injury should they fall off their horse. Describe three properties of a material that would be suitable for a riding helmet. Explain why each of these properties is advantageous. [6 marks]

My brain must be stiff — it's resistant to being stretched...

Hurrah... that's the last of the stress and strain... just electrical properties to go...

Electrical Properties of Solids

From a remote-controlled car to a supercomputer... if what you're building involves electricity, you're going to want to know about resistivity and conductivity...

Three Things Determine Resistance

If you think about a nice, **simple electrical component**, like a **length of wire**, its **resistance** depends on:

1) **Length (*l*).** The **longer** the wire the **more difficult** it is to make a **current flow**.
2) **Area (*A*).** The **wider** the wire the **easier** it will be for the electrons to pass along it.
3) **Resistivity (*ρ*) depends** on the **material.** The **structure** may make it easy or difficult for charge to flow. In general, resistivity depends on **environmental factors** as well, like **temperature** and **light intensity**.

The **resistivity** of a material is defined as the **resistance** of a **1 m length** with a **1 m² cross-sectional area**. It is measured in **ohm-metres (Ωm)**.

This is the Greek letter rho, the symbol for resistivity.

$$\rho = \frac{RA}{l}$$

where **A** = area in m², **l** = length in m

You'll more **usually** see the equation in the **form**:

$$R = \rho \frac{l}{A}$$

Black Beauty had a surprisingly low resistivity.

Typical values for the **resistivity** of **conductors** are **really small**, e.g., for **copper** (at 25 °C) $\rho = 1.72 \times 10^{-8}$ Ωm.

As we all know by now, conductance is the inverse of resistance. And surprise surprise... the inverse of resistivity is **conductivity, σ.**

The **conductivity** of a material is defined as the **conductance** of a **1 m length** with a **1 m² cross-sectional area**. It's measured in **siemens per metre (S m⁻¹)**.

$$\sigma = \frac{Gl}{A}$$

$$G = \sigma \frac{A}{l}$$

Experiment to find the Resistivity or Conductivity of a Material

Examiners love asking you how you'd measure the resistivity (or conductivity) of a material. You normally use a wire of the material you want to test because it's long and has a small cross-sectional area.

As resistance is proportional to $\frac{l}{A}$, this means that a wire will give you a large enough resistance (or a small enough conductance) for you to be able to measure.

Finding the Resistivity (or Conductivity) of a Wire

1) Measure out a length of wire made from the material you want to test with a millimetre ruler.
2) Use a **micrometer** to measure the **diameter** of a piece of wire in several places. Take an average of your measurements, and use that to work out the average **cross-sectional area** of the wire.
3) Connect a length of wire into an electrical circuit as shown, ensuring that current can flow through the entire length of the wire.
4) Record the voltage across the wire and the current flowing through it.
5) Use V = IR to find the resistance of the wire.
6) You can then use the resistance you've calculated and dimensions of wire to calculate the resistivity of the wire material.

You could test a few different lengths of wire and average the resistivity values you find to decrease the error in your final result (see p 74).

Electrical Properties of Solids

Different Materials have Different Numbers of Charge Carriers

How conductive a material is depends on its **charge carrier density** — how many charge carriers there are per unit volume of material. The more charge carriers a material has, the better a conductor it will be.

Metals

In a **metal**, the **charge carriers** are **free electrons** (see p 30). Metals are **good conductors** because they have absolutely shedloads of them — the **charge carrier density** is **high**.

If you **increase** the **temperature** of a metal, the **number** of charge carriers **stays about the same**. As the electrons move, they scatter from the metallic lattice. As the temperature increases, the lattice **vibrates** more, increasing the electron scattering, so the electrons are slightly less free to move. This means that as the **temperature increases**, the **conductivity** of a metal will slightly **decrease**.

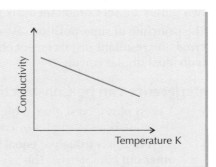

Semiconductors

Just as in metals, the charge carriers in **semiconductors** are free electrons. Semiconductors have a much **lower** charge carrier density (fewer free electrons) than metals, so they have a **lower conductivity**.

As you **increase** the **temperature** of a semiconductor, more electrons are freed to conduct. This means that as the temperature **increases**, the **conductivity** of a semiconductor **rapidly increases**.

Just as in metals, the semiconductor atom lattice will also vibrate more, scattering the free electrons as they move — but its effect is much smaller than the effect of the huge increase in charge carriers.

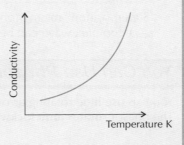

Insulators

A **perfect insulator** wouldn't have **any charge carriers**, so it wouldn't be able to conduct at all. (What can I say... it's short and sweet...)

Practice Questions

Q1 What three factors does the resistance of a length of wire depend on?

Q2 Describe how a metal's conductivity varies with temperature.

Q3 Write down the units of resistivity and conductivity.

Q4 Why are semiconductors poorer conductors than metals?

Exam Question

Q1 This question is about an experiment to measure the resistivity of copper.

(a) This experiment is normally done using copper wire.
Explain why this is a good shape of copper to use in this experiment. [2 marks]

(b) Describe the equipment and method you would use to measure the resistivity of a copper wire.
You should include a labelled circuit diagram as part of your answer. [3 marks]

Insulator Airlines — the no-charge carriers...

That resistivity experiment's a popular one to come up in exams — so make sure you learn it. Try to think about where errors are creeping into your measurements too, and how you might be able to reduce them... see p 74 for ideas...

Superposition and Coherence

When two waves get together, it can be either really impressive or really disappointing.

Superposition Happens When Two or More Waves Pass Through Each Other

1) At the **instant** the waves **cross**, the **displacements** due to each wave **combine**. Then **each wave** goes on its merry way. You can **see** this if **two pulses** are sent **simultaneously** from each end of a rope.

2) The **principle of superposition** says that when two or more **waves cross**, the **resultant** displacement equals the **vector sum** of the **individual** displacements.

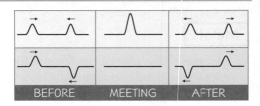

BEFORE   MEETING   AFTER

Interference can be Constructive or Destructive

1) A **crest** plus a **crest** gives a **big crest**. A **trough** plus a **trough** gives a **big trough**. These are both examples of **constructive interference**.

2) A **crest** plus a **trough** of **equal size** gives... **nothing**. The two displacements **cancel each other out** completely. This is called **destructive interference**.

3) If the **crest** and the **trough** aren't the **same size**, then the destructive interference **isn't total**. For the interference to be **noticeable**, the two **amplitudes** should be **nearly equal**.

Graphically, you can superimpose waves by adding the individual displacements at each point along the x-axis, and then plotting them.

"Superposition" means "one thing on top of another thing". You can use the same idea in reverse — a complex wave can be separated out mathematically into several simple sine waves of various sizes.

You Can Use Phasors to Show Superposition

You can use little rotating arrows to represent the phase of each point on a wave. These arrows are called **phasors**. The phasor **rotates anticlockwise** through one whole turn as the wave completes a full cycle.

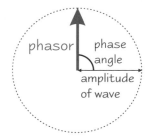

The length of the arrow shows the amplitude of the wave.

phasor | phase angle | amplitude of wave

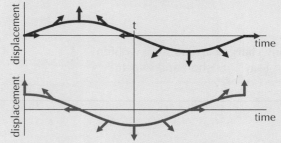

To superimpose waves using phasors, just add the arrows tip to tail:

To find the resultant at time t, add the phasors tip to tail:

$$\leftarrow + \downarrow = \nearrow$$

(So in this case, the resultant wave has a greater amplitude than the component waves and is 45° out of phase with both.)

In Phase Means In Step — Two Points In Phase Interfere Constructively

1) Two points on a wave are **in phase** if they are both at the **same point** in the **wave cycle**.

2) It's mathematically **handy** to show one **complete cycle** of a wave as an **angle of 360° (2π radians)**, the angle a phasor will travel through.

3) **Points** that have a **phase difference** of **zero** or a **multiple of 360°** are **in phase** — their phasors point in the **same direction**.

4) **Points** with a **phase difference** of **odd-number multiples of 180° (π radians)** are **exactly out of phase**, called **antiphase**. Their phasors point in **opposite directions**. And it's not just phase and antiphase — points can have a **phase difference** of **any** angle.

5) You can also talk about two **different waves** being **in phase**. **In practice** this happens because **both** waves came from the **same oscillator**. In **other** situations there will nearly always be a **phase difference** between two waves.

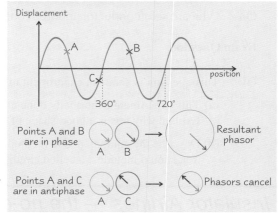

Points A and B are in phase → Resultant phasor

Points A and C are in antiphase → Phasors cancel

Superposition and Coherence

To Get Interference Patterns the Two Sources Must Be Coherent

Interference **still happens** when you're observing waves of **different wavelength** and **frequency** — but it happens in a **jumble**. In order to get clear **interference patterns**, the two or more sources must be **coherent**.

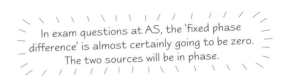
In exam questions at AS, the 'fixed phase difference' is almost certainly going to be zero. The two sources will be in phase.

Two sources are **coherent** if they have the **same wavelength** and **frequency** and a **fixed phase difference** between them.

Constructive or Destructive Interference Depends on the Path Difference

1) Whether you get **constructive** or **destructive** interference at a **point** depends on how **much further one wave** has travelled than the **other wave** to get to that point.

2) The **amount** by which the path travelled by one wave is **longer** than the path travelled by the other wave is called the **path difference.**

3) At **any point an equal distance** from both sources you will get **constructive interference.** You also get constructive interference at any point where the **path difference** is a **whole number of wavelengths**. At these points the two waves are **in phase** and **reinforce** each other. But at points where the path difference is **half a wavelength**, **one and a half** wavelengths, **two and a half** wavelengths etc., the waves arrive **out of phase** and you get **destructive interference**.

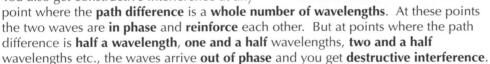

Speakers

Amplifier

Loud	Path diff = λ
Quiet	Path difference = $\frac{\lambda}{2}$
Loud	No path difference
Quiet	Path difference = $\frac{\lambda}{2}$
Loud	Path diff = λ

Constructive interference occurs when:

$$\text{path difference} = n\lambda \quad (\text{where } n \text{ is an integer})$$

Destructive interference occurs when:

$$\text{path difference} = \frac{(2n+1)\lambda}{2} = (n + \tfrac{1}{2})\lambda$$

Practice Questions

Q1 Why does the principle of superposition deal with the **vector** sum of two displacements?

Q2 What happens when a crest meets a slightly smaller trough?

Q3 If two points on a wave have a phase difference of 1440°, are they in phase?

Exam Questions

Q1 (a) Two sources are coherent.
What can you say about their frequencies, wavelengths and phase difference? [2 marks]

(b) Suggest why you might have difficulty in observing interference patterns in an area affected by two waves from two sources even though the two sources are coherent. [1 mark]

Q2 Two points on an undamped wave are exactly out of phase.

(a) What is the phase difference between them, expressed in degrees? [1 mark]

(b) Compare the direction and amplitude of the phasors of the two points. [2 marks]

Learn this and you'll be in a super position to pass your exam... ...I'll get my coat.

There are a few really crucial concepts here: a) interference can be constructive or destructive, b) constructive interference happens when the path difference is a whole number of wavelengths, c) the sources must be coherent.

Standing Waves

Standing waves are waves that... er... stand still... well, not still exactly... I mean, well... they don't go anywhere.

You get Standing Waves When a **Progressive Wave** is **Reflected** at a **Boundary**

A standing wave is the **superposition** of **two progressive waves** with the **same wavelength**, moving in **opposite directions**.

1) Unlike progressive waves, **no energy** is transmitted by a standing wave.

2) You can demonstrate standing waves by setting up a **driving oscillator** at one end of a **stretched string** with the other end fixed. The wave generated by the oscillator is **reflected** back and forth.

3) For most frequencies the resultant **pattern** is a **jumble**. However, if the oscillator happens to produce an **exact number of waves** in the time it takes for a wave to get to the **end** and **back again**, then the **original** and **reflected** waves **reinforce** each other.

4) At these **"resonant frequencies"** you get a **standing wave** where the **pattern doesn't move** — it just sits there, bobbing up and down. Happy, at peace with the world...

A sitting wave.

Standing Waves in **Strings** Form **Oscillating "Loops"** Separated by **Nodes**

1) Each particle vibrates at **right angles** to the string.
   Nodes are where the **amplitude** of the vibration is **zero**.
   Antinodes are points of **maximum amplitude**.

2) At resonant frequencies, an **exact number** of **half wavelengths** fits onto the string.

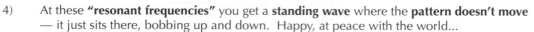

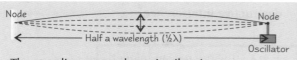

The standing wave above is vibrating at the **lowest possible** resonant frequency (the **fundamental frequency**). It has **one** "loop" with a **node** at each end.

This is the **second harmonic** (or **first overtone**). It is **twice** the fundamental frequency. There are two "**loops**" with a **node** in the **middle** and **one at each end**.

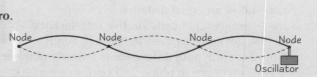

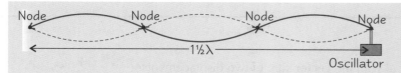

The **third harmonic** (or **second overtone**) is **three times** the fundamental frequency. **1½ wavelengths** fit on the string.

The **Notes** Played by **Stringed** and **Wind Instruments** are Standing Waves

Transverse standing waves form on the strings of **stringed instruments** like **violins** and **guitars**. Your finger or the bow sets the **string vibrating** at the point of contact. Waves are sent out in **both directions** and **reflected** back at both ends.

Longitudinal Standing Waves Form in a **Wind Instrument** or Other **Air Column**

1) If a source of sound is placed at the open end of a flute, piccolo, oboe or other column of air, there will be some **frequencies** for which **resonance** occurs and a standing wave is set up.

2) If the instrument has a **closed end**, a **node** will form there. You get the lowest resonant frequency when the length, *l*, of the pipe is a **quarter wavelength**.

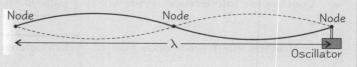

$$l = \frac{\lambda}{4}$$

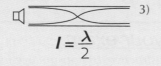

$$l = \frac{\lambda}{2}$$

3) **Antinodes** form at the **open ends** of pipes. If both ends are open, you get the lowest resonant frequency when the length, *l*, of the pipe is a **half wavelength**.

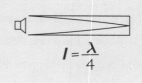

Remember, the sound waves in wind instruments are <u>longitudinal</u> — they <u>don't</u> actually look like these diagrams.

Standing Waves

You can Demonstrate Standing Waves with Microwaves

Microwaves Reflected Off a Metal Plate Set Up a Standing Wave

Microwave standing wave apparatus ➡

You can find the **nodes** and **antinodes** by moving the **probe** between the **transmitter** and the **reflecting** plate.

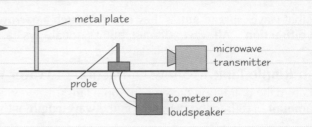

metal plate

microwave transmitter

probe

to meter or loudspeaker

You can Use Standing Waves to Measure the Speed of Sound

Finding the Speed of Sound in a Resonance Tube

1) You can create a closed-end pipe by placing a **hollow tube** into a measuring cylinder of water.

2) Choose a tuning fork and note down the frequency of sound it produces (it'll be stamped on the side of it).

3) Gently tap the tuning fork and hold it just above the hollow tube. The sound waves produced by the fork travel down the tube and get reflected (and form a **node**) at the air/water surface.

4) Move the tube up and down until you find the **shortest distance** between the top of the tube and the water level that the sound from the fork **resonates** at.

5) Just like with any closed pipe, this distance is a **quarter** of the **wavelength** of the standing sound wave.

6) Once you know the **frequency** and **wavelength** of the standing sound wave, you can work out the **speed of sound** (in air), v, using the equation $v = f\lambda$.

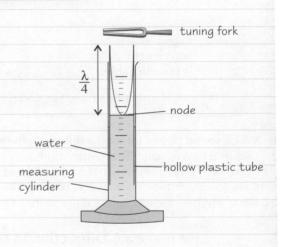

tuning fork

$\frac{\lambda}{4}$

node

water

measuring cylinder

hollow plastic tube

Practice Questions

Q1 How do standing waves form?

Q2 At four times the fundamental frequency, how many half wavelengths fit on a violin string?

Q3 Describe an experiment to find the speed of sound in air using standing waves.

Exam Question

Q1 (a) A standing wave of three times the fundamental frequency is formed on a stretched string of length 1.2 m. Sketch a diagram showing the form of the wave. [2 marks]

(b) What is the wavelength of the standing wave? [1 mark]

(c) Explain how the amplitude varies along the string. How is that different from the amplitude of a progressive wave? [2 marks]

CGP — putting the FUN back in FUNdamental frequency...

Resonance was a big problem for the Millennium Bridge in London. The resonant frequency of the bridge was round about normal walking pace, so as soon as people started using it they set up a huge standing wave. An oversight, I feel...

Diffraction

Astronomers trying to observe radio waves have to battle diffraction. They've been known to cheat and set up a network of telescopes around the world to get a good image. All that trouble because of diffraction... but it has its uses too.

Waves Go **Round Corners** and **Spread out** of **Gaps**

The way that **waves spread out** as they come through a **narrow gap** or go round obstacles is called **diffraction**. **All** waves diffract, but it's not always easy to observe.

Use a **Ripple Tank** To Show Diffraction of **Water Waves**

You can make diffraction patterns in ripple tanks.
The **amount** of diffraction depends on the **wavelength** of the wave compared with the **size of the gap**.

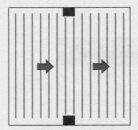

When the gap is **a lot bigger** than the **wavelength**, diffraction is **unnoticeable**.

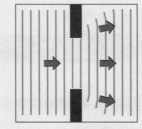

You get **noticeable diffraction** through a gap **several** wavelengths wide.

You get the **most** diffraction when the gap is **the same** size as the **wavelength**.

If the gap is **smaller** than the wavelength, the waves are mostly just **reflected back**.

When **sound** passes through a **doorway**, the **size of gap** and the **wavelength** are usually roughly **equal**, so **a lot** of **diffraction** occurs. That's why you have no trouble **hearing** someone through an **open door** to the next room, even if the other person is out of your **line of sight**. The reason that you can't **see** him or her is that when **light** passes through the doorway, it is passing through a **gap** around a **hundred million times bigger** than its wavelength — the amount of diffraction is **tiny**.

Demonstrate **Diffraction** in **Light** Using **Laser Light**

1) Diffraction in **light** can be demonstrated by shining a **laser light** through a very **narrow slit** onto a screen (see page 41). You can alter the amount of diffraction by changing the width of the slit.

2) You can do a similar experiment using a **white light** source instead of the laser (which is monochromatic) and a set of **colour filters**. The size of the slit can be kept constant while the **wavelength** is varied by putting different **colour filters** over the slit.

Warning. Use of coloured filters may result in excessive fun.

You Get a **Similar** Effect Around an **Obstacle**

When a wave meets an **obstacle**, you get diffraction around the edges.

Behind the obstacle is a 'shadow', where the wave is blocked. The **wider** the obstacle compared with the wavelength of the wave, the less diffraction you get, and so the **longer** the shadow.

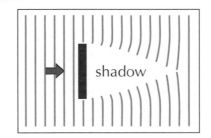

shadow

Diffraction

With *Light Waves* you get a *Pattern* of *Light* and *Dark Fringes*

1) If the **wavelength** of a **light wave** is roughly similar to the size of the **aperture**, you get a **diffraction pattern** of light and dark fringes.

2) The pattern has a **bright central fringe** with alternating **dark and bright fringes** on either side of it.

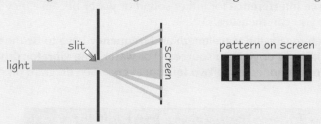

You need to use a coherent light source for this experiment.

3) The **narrower** the slit, the **wider** the diffraction pattern.

You can Explain Diffraction Patterns Using Phasors...

1) The **brightest** point of a diffraction pattern is where light passes in a straight line from the slit to the screen. All the light waves that arrive there are **in phase**.

2) At all other bright points where light hits the screen, there is a **constant phase difference** between the waves arriving there, so the phasors point in slightly different directions and form a **smaller resultant**.

3) **Dark fringes** on the screen are where the phase difference between the light waves means their phasors add to form a **circle**, giving a **resultant of zero**.

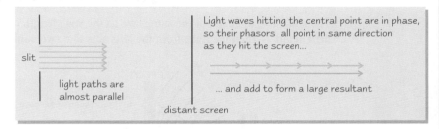

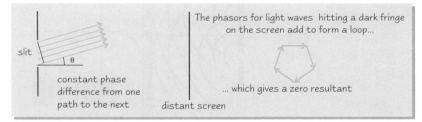

Practice Questions

Q1 What is diffraction?

Q2 Sketch what happens when plane waves meet an obstacle about as wide as one wavelength.

Q3 For a long time some scientists argued that light couldn't be a wave because it did not seem to diffract. Suggest why they might have got this impression.

Q4 Describe in terms of phasors why diffraction patterns are made up of bright and dark fringes.

Exam Question

Q1 A mountain lies directly between you and a radio transmitter.

Explain using diagrams why you can pick up long-wave radio broadcasts from the transmitter but not short-wave radio broadcasts.

[4 marks]

Even hiding behind a mountain, you can't get away from long-wave radio...

*Diffraction crops up again in particle physics, quantum physics and astronomy, so you **really** need to understand it.*

Two-Source Interference

That Young chap gets everywhere... and here he is again. Young was a doctor, and nowadays you probably wouldn't trust a doctor who started telling you he was right and other physicists including Newton were wrong... I mean Newton's Mr Gravity for goodness' sake. But it turned out he was right... and this was the experiment that helped him show it.

Demonstrating Two-Source Interference in **Water** and **Sound** is Easy

1) It's **easy** to demonstrate **two-source interference** for either **sound** or **water** because they've got **wavelengths** of a handy **size** that you can **measure**.

2) You need **coherent** sources, which means the **wavelength** and **frequency** have to be the **same**. The trick is to use the **same oscillator** to drive **both sources**. For **water**, one **vibrator** drives two **dippers**. For sound, **one oscillator** is connected to **two loudspeakers**. (See diagram on page 37.)

Demonstrating **Two-Source** Interference for **Light** is Harder

Young's Double-Slit Experiment

1) You **can't** arrange **two separate coherent light sources** because **light** from **each source** is emitted in **random bursts**. Instead a **single** laser is shone through **two slits**.

2) Laser light is **coherent** and **monochromatic** (there's only **one wavelength** present).

3) The slits have to be about the same size as the wavelength of the laser light so that it is **diffracted** — then the light from the slits acts like **two coherent point sources**.

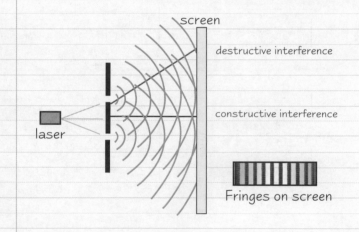

4) You get a pattern of light and dark **fringes**, depending on whether constructive or destructive **interference** is taking place. Thomas Young — the first person to do this experiment (with a lamp rather than a laser) — came up with an **equation** to **work out** the **wavelength** of the **light** from this experiment (see next page).

You Can Do a **Similar** Experiment with **Microwaves**

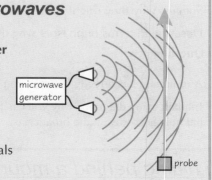

1) To see interference patterns with **microwaves**, you can **replace** the laser and slits with two microwave **transmitter cones** attached to the **same** signal generator.

2) You also need to replace the screen with a microwave **receiver probe** (like the one used in the standing waves experiment on page 39).

3) If you move the probe along the path of the green arrow, you'll get an **alternating pattern** of **strong** and **weak** signals — just like the light and dark fringes on the screen.

Two-Source Interference

Work Out the Wavelength with Young's Double-Slit Formula

1) The fringe spacing (**X**), wavelength (**λ**), spacing between slits (**d**) and the distance from slits to screen (**D**) are all related by **Young's double-slit formula**, which works for all waves (you need to know it, but not derive it).

$$\text{Fringe spacing, } X = \frac{D\lambda}{d}$$

"Fringe spacing" means the distance from the centre of one minimum to the centre of the next minimum or from the centre of one maximum to the centre of the next maximum.

Always check your fringe spacing.

2) Since the wavelength of light is so small you can see from the formula that a high ratio of **D / d** is needed to make the fringe spacing **big enough to see**.

3) Rearranging, you can use **λ = Xd / D** to **calculate the wavelength** of light.

4) The fringes are **so tiny** that it's very hard to get an **accurate value of X**. It's easier to measure across **several** fringes then **divide** by the number of **fringe widths** between them.

Young's Experiment was Evidence for the Wave Nature of Light

1) Towards the end of the **17th century**, two important **theories of light** were published — one by Isaac Newton and the other by a chap called Huygens. **Newton's** theory suggested that light was made up of tiny particles, which he called "**corpuscles**". And **Huygens** put forward a theory using **waves**.

2) The **corpuscular theory** could explain **reflection** and **refraction**, but **diffraction** and **interference** are both **uniquely** wave properties. If it could be **shown** that light showed interference patterns, that would help settle the argument once and for all.

3) **Young's** double-slit experiment (over 100 years later) provided the necessary evidence. It showed that light could both **diffract** (through the narrow slits) and **interfere** (to form the interference pattern on the screen).

Of course, this being Physics, nothing's ever simple — give it another 100 years or so and the debate would be raging again. But that can wait for page 46...

Practice Questions

Q1 In Young's experiment, why do you get a bright fringe at a point equidistant from both slits?

Q2 What does Young's experiment show about the nature of light?

Q3 Write down Young's double-slit formula.

Exam Questions

Q1 (a) The diagram on the right shows waves from two coherent light sources, S_1 and S_2. Sketch the interference pattern, marking on constructive and destructive interference.
[2 marks]

(b) In practice if interference is to be observed, S_1 and S_2 must be slits in a screen behind which there is a source of laser light. Why? [2 marks]

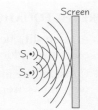

Q2 In an experiment to study sound interference, two loudspeakers are connected to an oscillator emitting sound at 1320 Hz and set up as shown in the diagram below. They are 1.5 m apart and 7 m away from the line AC. A listener moving from A to C hears minimum sound at A and C and maximum sound at B.

(a) Calculate the wavelength of the sound waves if the speed of sound in air is taken to be 330 ms^{-1}. [1 mark]

(b) Calculate the separation of points A and C. [2 marks]

Carry on Physics — this page is far too saucy...

Be careful when you're calculating the fringe width by averaging over several fringes. Don't just divide by the number of bright lines. Ten bright lines will only have nine fringe-widths between them, not ten. It's an easy mistake to make, but you have been warned... mwa ha ha (felt necessary, sorry).

Diffraction Gratings

Diffraction gratings are pretty amazing. If you want to know what a star's made of you obviously can't just go there with your bucket and spade. Luckily astronomers can tell just by looking at light emitted from the star using one of these babies what the star's atmosphere's made of... genius.

Interference Patterns Get **Sharper** When You Diffract Through **More Slits**

1) You can repeat **Young's double-slit** experiment (see p 42) with **more than two equally spaced** slits. You get basically the **same shaped** pattern as for two slits — but the **bright bands** are **brighter** and **narrower** and the **dark areas** between are **darker**.

2) When **monochromatic light** (one wavelength) is passed through a **grating** with **hundreds** of slits per millimetre, the interference pattern is **really sharp** because there are so **many beams reinforcing** the **pattern**.

3) Sharper fringes make for more **accurate** measurements.

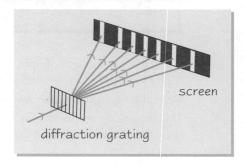
screen
diffraction grating

Monochromatic Light on a Diffraction Grating gives Sharp Lines

1) For **monochromatic** light, all the **maxima** are sharp lines. (It's different for white light — see next page.)

2) There's a line of **maximum brightness** at the centre called the **zero order** line.

3) The lines just **either side** of the central one are called **first order lines**. The **next pair out** are called **second order** lines and so on.

4) For a grating with slits a distance **d** apart, the angle between the **incident beam** and **the nth order maximum** is given by:

$$d \sin \theta = n\lambda$$

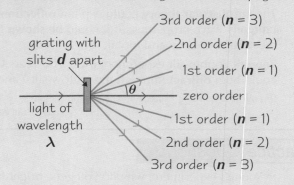
grating with slits **d** apart
light of wavelength λ
3rd order (**n** = 3)
2nd order (**n** = 2)
1st order (**n** = 1)
zero order
1st order (**n** = 1)
2nd order (**n** = 2)
3rd order (**n** = 3)

5) So by observing **d**, **θ** and **n** you can **calculate the wavelength** of the light.

If the grating has N slits per metre, then the slit spacing, d, is just 1/N metres.

WHERE THE EQUATION COMES FROM:

1) At **each slit**, the incoming waves are **diffracted**. These diffracted waves then **interfere** with each other to produce an **interference pattern**.

2) Consider the **first order maximum**. This happens at the **angle** when the waves from one slit line up with waves from the **next slit** that are **exactly one wavelength** behind.

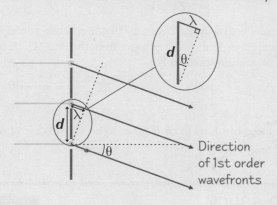
Direction of 1st order wavefronts

3) Call the **angle** between the **first order maximum** and the **incoming light** θ.

4) Now, look at the **triangle** highlighted in the diagram. The angle is θ (using basic geometry), **d** is the slit spacing and the **path difference** is λ.

5) So, for the first maximum, using trig:
$$d \sin \theta = \lambda$$

6) The other maxima occur when the path difference is 2λ, 3λ, 4λ, etc. So to make the equation **general**, just replace λ with nλ, where **n** is an integer — the **order** of the maximum.

Diffraction Gratings

You can Draw General Conclusions from d sin θ = nλ

1) If λ is **bigger**, sin θ is **bigger**, and so θ is **bigger**. This means that the larger the **wavelength**, the more the pattern will **spread out**.

2) If d is **bigger**, sin θ is **smaller**. This means that the **coarser** the **grating**, the **less** the pattern will **spread out**.

3) Values of **sin θ** greater than **1** are **impossible**. So if for a certain n you get a result of **more than 1** for sin θ you know that that order **doesn't exist**.

Shining White Light Through a Diffraction Grating Produces Spectra

1) **White light** is really a **mixture** of **colours**. If you **diffract** white light through a **grating** then the patterns due to **different wavelengths** within the white light are **spread out** by **different** amounts.

2) Each **order** in the pattern becomes a **spectrum**, with **red** on the **outside** and **violet** on the **inside**. The **zero order maximum** stays **white** because all the wavelengths just pass straight through.

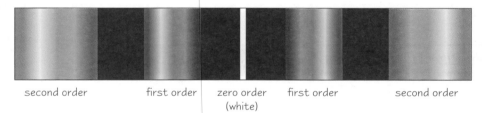

second order   first order   zero order   first order   second order
(white)

Astronomers and **chemists** often need to study spectra to help identify elements. They use diffraction gratings rather than prisms because they're **more accurate**.

Practice Questions

Q1 How is the diffraction grating pattern for white light different from the pattern for laser light?

Q2 What difference does it make to the pattern if you use a finer grating?

Q3 What equation is used to find the angle between the nth order maximum and the incident beam for a diffraction grating?

Q4 Derive the equation you quoted in Q3.

Exam Questions

Q1 Yellow laser light of wavelength 600 nm (6×10^{-7} m) is transmitted through a diffraction grating of 4×10^5 lines per metre.

(a) At what angle to the normal are the first and second order bright lines seen?   [4 marks]

(b) Is there a fifth order line?   [1 mark]

Q2 Visible, monochromatic light is transmitted through a diffraction grating of 3.7×10^5 lines per metre. The first order maximum is at an angle of 14.2° to the incident beam.

Find the wavelength of the incident light.   [2 marks]

Oooooooooooooo — pretty patterns...

Three important points for you to take away — the more slits you have, the sharper the image, one lovely equation to learn and white light makes a pretty spectrum. Make sure you get everything in this section — there's some good stuff coming up in the next one and I wouldn't want you to be distracted.

Light and Photons

You probably already thought light was a bit weird — but oh no... being a wave that travels at the fastest speed possible isn't enough for light — it has to go one step further and act like a particle too...

Light Travels at High Speed

1) Light travels really quickly — around 3.00×10^8 ms^{-1}.

2) And that makes its speed really hard to measure.
   You only really notice that light takes **time** to travel anywhere if it's travelling over a **very large distance** (like in astronomy), or if you've got a really accurate clock.
   (There's also a rather clever method for measuring its speed using interference, but you don't need to know about that.)

> **Example** Light takes roughly 1.25 seconds to travel from the Moon to the Earth. The Moon's average distance from the Earth is 3.8×10^8 m. Find the speed of light, c.
>
> Speed of light, $c = 3.8 \times 10^8 \div 1.25 = 3.0 \times 10^8$ ms^{-1} (to 2 s.f.)

Light might be faster, but Sheila doubted it could look quite as fetching in shorts

Light Behaves Like a Wave... or a Stream of Particles

1) In the **late nineteenth century**, if you asked what light was, scientists would happily show you lots of nice experiments showing how light must be a **wave** (see pages 36–45).

2) Then came the **photoelectric effect**, which mucked up everything.
   The only way you could explain this effect was if light acted as a **particle** — called a **photon**.

The Photoelectric Effect

If you shine **light** of a **high enough frequency** onto the **surface of a metal**, it will **emit electrons**. For **most** metals, this **frequency** falls in the **U.V.** range.

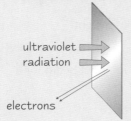

ultraviolet radiation

electrons

1) **Free electrons** on the **surface** of the metal **absorb energy** from the light, making them **vibrate**.

2) If an electron **absorbs enough** energy, the **bonds** holding it to the metal **break** and the electron is **released**.

3) This is called the **photoelectric effect** and the electrons emitted are called **photoelectrons**.

You don't need to know the details of any experiments on this — you just need to learn the three main conclusions:

Conclusion 1	For a given metal, **no photoelectrons are emitted** if the radiation has a frequency **below** a certain value — called the **threshold frequency**.
Conclusion 2	The photoelectrons are emitted with a variety of kinetic energies ranging from zero to some maximum value. This value of **maximum kinetic energy** increases with the **frequency** of the radiation, and is **unaffected** by the **intensity** of the radiation.
	The **number** of photoelectrons emitted per second is **proportional** to the **intensity** of the radiation.

These are the two that had scientists puzzled. They can't be explained using wave theory.

QUANTUM BEHAVIOUR

Light and Photons

The Photoelectric Effect Could only be Explained Using Photons...

According to wave theory:

1) For a particular frequency of light, the **energy** carried is **proportional** to the **intensity** of the beam.
2) The energy carried by the light would be **spread evenly** over the wavefront.
3) **Each** free electron on the surface of the metal would gain a **bit of energy** from each incoming wave.
4) Gradually, each electron would gain **enough energy** to leave the metal.

SO... If the light had a **lower frequency** (i.e. was carrying less energy) it would take **longer** for the electrons to gain enough energy — but it would happen eventually. There is **no explanation** for the **threshold frequency**.

The **higher the intensity** of the wave, the **more energy** it should transfer to each electron — the kinetic energy should increase with **intensity**. There's **no explanation** for the **kinetic energy** depending only on the **frequency**.

A Photon is a Quantum of EM Radiation

1) When Einstein was looking at this problem, it had already been suggested that **EM waves** can **only** be **released** in **discrete packets**, called **quanta.** A single packet of **EM radiation** is called a **quantum**.
2) **Einstein** went **further** by suggesting that **EM waves** (and the energy they carry) can only **exist** in discrete packets. He called these wave-packets **photons**.

The **energy carried** by one of these **wave-packets** had to be:

$$E = hf = \frac{hc}{\lambda}$$

where h = Planck's constant = 6.63×10^{-34} Js,
f = frequency (Hz), λ = wavelength (m)
and c = speed of light in a vacuum = 3.00×10^8 ms^{-1}

3) So, the **higher** the **frequency** of the electromagnetic radiation, the more **energy** its wave-packets carry.
4) He believed that a photon acts as **particle**, and will either transfer **all** or **none** of its energy when interacting with another particle, like an electron.

According to the photon model:

1) When light hits its surface, the metal is **bombarded** by photons.
2) If one of these photons **collides** with a free electron, the electron will gain energy equal to *hf*.

Before an electron can **leave** the surface of the metal, it needs enough energy to **break the bonds holding it there**. This energy is called the **work function energy** (symbol ϕ) and its **value** depends on the **metal**.

Practice Questions

Q1 Give two different ways to describe the nature of light.

Q2 Write down the two formulae you can use to find the energy of a photon.
Include the meanings of all the symbols you use.

Q3 Write down the three conclusions you can make from an experiment showing the photoelectric effect.

Exam Question

Q1 Explain why the photoelectric effect only occurs after the incident light
has reached a certain frequency. [3 marks]

Photon-tastic...

I hate it in physics when they tell you lies, make you learn it, and just when you've got to grips with it they tell you it was all a load of codswallop. This is the real deal folks — light isn't just the nice wave you've always known...

Energy Levels and Photon Emission

Hot gas doesn't sound like one of the nicest discussion points, but look how pretty it is. All together now: red and yellow and pink and green, orange and purple and bluuuuuuuuuuuuuuuuuuuue...

Electrons in Atoms Exist in Discrete Energy Levels

1) **Electrons** in an **atom** can **only exist** in certain **well-defined energy levels**. Each level is given a **number**, with **n = 1** representing the **ground state**.

2) Electrons can **move down** an energy level by **emitting** a **photon**.

3) Since these **transitions** are between **definite energy levels**, the **energy** of **each photon** emitted can **only** take a **certain allowed value**.

4) The diagram on the right shows the **energy levels** for **atomic hydrogen**.

5) The **energy** carried by each **photon** is **equal** to the **difference in energies** between the **two levels**. The equation below shows a **transition** between levels **n = 2** and **n = 1**:

$$\Delta E = E_2 - E_1 = hf = \frac{hc}{\lambda}$$

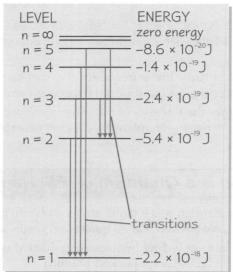

LEVEL	ENERGY
n = ∞	zero energy
n = 5	-8.6×10^{-20} J
n = 4	-1.4×10^{-19} J
n = 3	-2.4×10^{-19} J
n = 2	-5.4×10^{-19} J
n = 1	-2.2×10^{-18} J

transitions

The energies are only negative because of how "zero energy" is defined. Just one of those silly convention things — don't worry about it.

Hot Gases Produce Line Emission Spectra

1) If you heat a gas to a high temperature, many of it's electrons move to higher energy levels.

2) As they fall back to the ground state, these electrons emit energy as photons.

3) If you **split** the light from a **hot gas** with a **prism** or a **diffraction grating** (see pages 44-45), you get a **line spectrum**. A line spectrum is seen as a **series** of **bright lines** against a **black background**, as shown below.

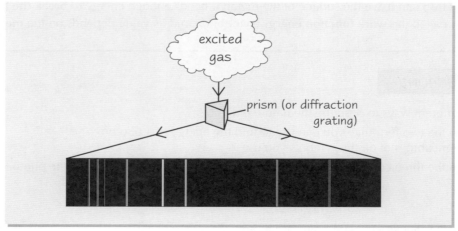

excited gas

prism (or diffraction grating)

4) Each **line** on the spectrum corresponds to a **particular wavelength** of light **emitted** by the source. Since only **certain photon energies** are **allowed**, you only see the **corresponding wavelengths**.

Energy Levels and Photon Emission

Shining **White Light** through a **Cool Gas** gives an **Absorption Spectrum**

Continuous Spectra Contain All Possible Wavelengths

1) The **spectrum** of **white light** is **continuous**.

2) If you **split** the **light** up with a **prism**, the **colours** all **merge** into each other — there **aren't** any **gaps** in the spectrum.

3) **Hot things** emit a **continuous spectrum** in the visible and infrared.

Decreasing wavelength ⟹

Cool Gases Remove Certain Wavelengths from the Continuous Spectrum

1) You get a **line absorption spectrum** when **light** with a **continuous** spectrum of **energy** (white light) passes through a cool gas.

2) At **low temperatures**, **most** of the **electrons** in the **gas atoms** will be in their **ground states**.

3) **Photons** of the **correct wavelength** are **absorbed** by the **electrons** to **excite** them to **higher energy levels**.

4) These **wavelengths** are then **missing** from the **continuous spectrum** when it **comes out** the other side of the gas.

5) You see a **continuous spectrum** with **black lines** in it corresponding to the **absorbed wavelengths**.

6) If you **compare** the **absorption** and **emission** spectra of a **particular gas**, the **black lines** in the **absorption spectrum match up** to the **bright lines** in the **emission spectrum**.

white light → cool gas

excited gas →

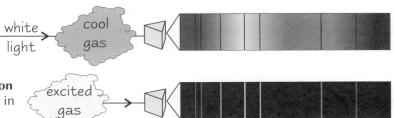

Practice Questions

Q1 Describe line absorption and line emission spectra. How are these two types of spectra produced?

Q2 Why do different excited gases glow different colours?

Exam Question

Q1 An electron has a kinetic energy of 1.94×10^{-18} J. This electron hits a hydrogen atom and excites it.

(a) Explain what is meant by excitation. [1 mark]

(b) Using the energy values on the right, work out to which energy level the electron in the hydrogen atom is excited. [1 mark]

(c) Calculate the energies of the three photons that might be emitted as the electron returns to its ground state. [3 marks]

$n = 5$ ——————— -8.65×10^{-20} J
$n = 4$ ——————— -1.36×10^{-19} J
$n = 3$ ——————— -2.40×10^{-19} J
$n = 2$ ——————— -5.45×10^{-19} J
$n = 1$ ——————— -2.18×10^{-18} J

I can honestly say I've never got so excited that I've produced light...

This is heavy stuff, it really is. Quite interesting though, as I was just saying to Dom a moment ago. He's doing a psychology book. Psychology's probably quite interesting too — and easier. But it won't help you become an astrophysicist.

The "Sum Over Paths" Theory

So... you've got to grips with phasors... now here's where the really weird stuff kicks in. Buckle your seatbelts...and prepare to be amazed as the magical world of quantum reveals why light travels in straight lines, and why probability is a bit more useful than guessing what coloured ball you're likely to pick out of a bag...

Photons *try* Every Possible Path

1) A rather clever bloke called Richard Feynman came up with a completely different idea of how photons (or any subatomic particles, **quanta**) get from a source to a detector.

2) Feynman reckoned that instead of just taking one route to the detector, a photon will take **all** of the **possible paths** to the detector in one go. You can keep track of this photon whizzing along every possible route using **phasors** (see p 36).

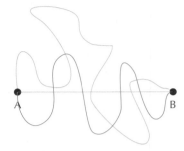

And all means <u>all</u> — the paths between A and B can be as squiggly as you like.

You *can use* Phasors *to track* Quanta

1) Take **Young's double-slit experiment** (see p 42). You can use phasors to show how light or dark a certain spot on a screen will be. In quantum mechanics, you can use phasors to tell you how **probable** it is that a quantum (in this case a photon) will arrive there.

2) Take a photon travelling down **one particular path**.
   As it travels, its phasor will rotate (anticlockwise) until it reaches the detector. By knowing the energy of the photon, you can work out the **frequency** of the phasor's rotation, *f*, by rearranging Planck's formula.

$$f = \frac{E}{h}$$

Remember — E is the photon's energy and h is Planck's constant

3) You want to **record** the position of the phasor at the **end** of every path — you could then **sum** these phasors to find the **resultant phasor** for the photon making the journey from a source to a detector.

4) Of course you can't find the final phasor for every path as there's an **infinite** number of them. When you do the maths, nearly all the phasors cancel each other out — so you only need to consider the straightest/quickest possible paths (see p 52).

Example: Young's Double-Slit Experiment (again...)

1) Imagine that a photon is emitted by the source and hits point X on the screen. Take two of its possible paths and say it follows **both** of them, as shown.

2) The **phasor** of the photon along each path rotates at the **same rate** (because it's the **same photon** so the phasors will have the same frequency).

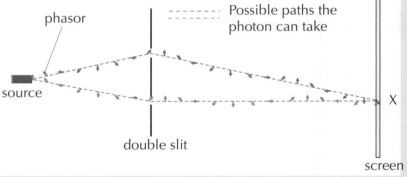

phasor

Possible paths the photon can take

source

double slit

X

screen

3) Because the photon has to travel slightly **further** on the green path, it takes slightly **longer** to reach point X. This means the final phasor for the green path will have **rotated** slightly **further** than that for the blue path.

4) You can find the **resultant** phasor arrow for the photon reaching point X by **adding** the final phasor position for each path, **tip-to-tail** (just like a normal vector sum (see p 56)).

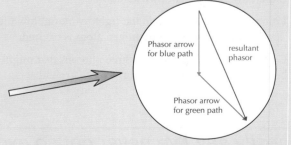

Phasor arrow for blue path

resultant phasor

Phasor arrow for green path

The "Sum Over Paths" Theory

You can Calculate Probability from the Resultant Phasor

1) You can find the **probability** that a quantum will arrive at a point from **squaring** the **resultant phasor amplitude**.

$$\text{Probability} \propto (\text{Resultant phasor})^2$$

2) The **higher** the probability, the **more likely** the particle will arrive there (well der....).

3) If the **photon** is your quantum of choice, you can think of the **probability** and the **brightness** of the area as pretty much the same thing — the more **probable** it is that a photon will arrive at a point, the **brighter** it will appear.

Example

resultant phasor for
photon hitting point X

magnitude = 2.5

resultant phasor for
photon hitting point Y

magnitude = 1.34

The resultant phasor amplitudes are shown for the paths a photon could take to points X and Y. How many times brighter does point X appear than point Y? Explain your answer.

Square the magnitude of each phasor to find a number proportional to the probability of the photon arriving at each point.

Probability of photon hitting point X $\propto (2.5)^2 = $ **6.25**

Probability of photon hitting point Y $\propto (1.34)^2 = $ **1.80** (3 s.f.)

The more probable a photon will arrive at a point, the brighter it will be. So the relative probability of a photon arriving at the two points will be the relative brightness between the points.

So, point X appears 6.25 ÷ 1.80 = **3.5 times** brighter than point Y.

Practice Questions

Q1 What equation would you use to find the frequency of rotation of a photon phasor?

Q2 How are two phasor arrows combined to give a resultant?

Q3 How will a point appear if the probability for a light photon is zero there?

Exam Questions

Q1 The resultant phasors for an electron reaching points A and B have magnitudes of 6.3 and 4.5 respectively. How many times more likely is it that an electron will arrive at point A than point B? [4 marks]

Q2 A light photon has a frequency of 6.0×10^{14} Hz. How many times does the photon's phasor arrow rotate as it moves along a path 120 mm long from a source to a detector? ($c = 3.0 \times 10^8$ ms^{-1}.) [2 marks]

Q3 An electron has a velocity of 4.0×10^5 ms^{-1}. The mass of an electron is 9.1×10^{-31} kg and h = 6.6×10^{-34} Js.

(a) Calculate the kinetic energy of the electron. [1 mark]

(b) What is the frequency of rotation of its phasor? [2 marks]

Set your phasors to stun...

This all sounds a bit weird, but I guess it's only as bizarre sounding as saying light's a particle or a wave depending on its mood at the time. It also gives a brand new way of looking at your everyday physics fun like reflection...

Using "Sum Over Paths"

Feynman could have just been having a laugh, but the results from his theory hold up just as well as any other...

Reflections in a Plane Mirror — Same Angle Reflection is the Preferred Path

1) Imagine you're firing a photon at a mirror so that it **reflects** and hits a detector.

2) You normally just assume that when light bounces off a mirror, it takes the **quickest** possible path, where the **angle of incidence, *i*, equals** the **angle of reflection, *r*** (Path 3). But the sum over paths rule says a photon will take **every possible path**...

3) As before, you need to find the final position of the photon's phasor for **every possible path** (of course in practice you only look at a few), then add the final phasors to find the resultant.

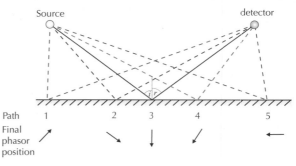

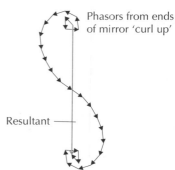

4) What you find is that the paths **nearest** to the **quickest** path have phasors that almost **line up**, giving most of the amplitude of the resultant — and so **most** of the **probability** that the photon will reach the detector.

5) The final phasors for slower, longer paths near the ends of the mirror tend to **'curl up'** and almost cancel themselves out. They end up adding **almost nothing** to the resultant amplitude or the probability.

6) So quantum behaviour shows that **most** of the probability that a photon will arrive at the detector comes from the path you'd **classically expect** the light to take — the sum over paths rule **predicts** the rule of reflection.

The Path that gives the Highest Probability is the Quickest Route

1) The sum over paths rule predicts all sorts of physics laws we take for granted. And each time it seems to be down to the **same reason**:

> The final phasor of the **quickest path** will contribute the **most** to the **resultant amplitude** and the **probability** of a quantum arriving at a point.

2) It even predicts one of the most fundamental light behaviours — that **light** travels in a **straight line**. If you find the final phasors for every possible path, you get a similar pattern to the reflection experiment above. As a **straight line** is the shortest (and therefore **quickest**) path between two points — it provides the largest probability of a photon arriving at a particular point.

3) Obviously there are times when light **doesn't** travel in a straight line, like when it's being **refracted** — but quantum behaviour predicts that as well...

Example: Refraction

1) Imagine spotting a pineapple at the bottom of a swimming pool. What **route** does the light take from the pineapple to your eye? Altogether now... it takes **all of them**.

2) When light travels in water, it **slows down**, but its **frequency stays the same**. This means the photons still have the **same energy**, and a photon's phasor will still have the **same amplitude** and **frequency** of rotation **whatever** material it's travelling through.

3) If you add up all the phasors for all the possible paths, it's the path that takes the **shortest time** that contributes the most to the resultant amplitude and so to the probability that the photon will get to your eye.

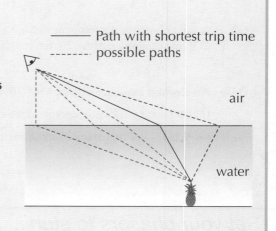

—— Path with shortest trip time
------- possible paths

air

water

Using "Sum Over Paths"

You Need *All Paths* to Take the *Same Time* to Focus *Quanta*

To **focus** photons (or any other quanta), you need to make sure all straight line paths (that follow the reflection or refraction rule) from the source to the focus point take the **same amount of time** — so the final phasors for every path will be in the same direction.

Example 1 — A Concave Mirror

The curve of a concave mirror has to be such that no matter which part of the mirror a photon hits, it will have taken the same time (and so travelled the same distance) when it reaches the focal point of the mirror.

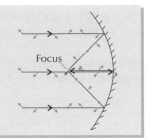

Example 2 — A Convex Lens

The paths towards the edges of the lens are **longer** than those that go through the middle. You make the time taken for each path the same by **increasing** the amount of **glass** in the **middle part** of the lens to increase the time it takes to travel along the shorter paths between the source and detector.

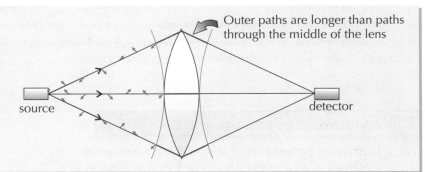

Outer paths are longer than paths through the middle of the lens

Practice Questions

Q1   Explain how the sum over paths theory predicts that light should travel in a straight line.

Q2   Describe how the sum over paths rule explains the path of reflected light.

Q3   Describe in terms of phasors how light is focused through a convex lens.

Exam Question

Q1   A photon travels from a source S through three slits onto a screen.
The phasors for three paths the photon can take to each of two points
on the screen, B and D, are shown below.
(0.5 cm is equal to an amplitude of 3.)

Point B   Point D

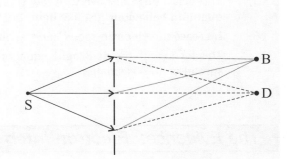

(a) Find the resultant phasor amplitude at
   i)   point B.   [1 mark]
   ii) point D.   [1 mark]

(b) Explain why point B on the screen appears dimmer than point D.   [2 marks]

I ate all the pies — some would call it greed, I say it's photon thinking...

OK, so that's some pretty wacky sounding physics... but it does seem to work and agree with the standard physics laws we know and love... well, maybe not <u>love</u>. It's tricky, but you just need to follow the same method each time: sum the final phasors for all possible paths to get the resultant, then use the resultant to find the probability the quanta will get there.

Quantum Behaviour of Electrons

Light isn't the only thing that shows quantum behaviour — electrons do too...

De Broglie *Suggested* Electrons *were* Quantum Objects

1) Louis de Broglie made a **bold suggestion** in his **PhD thesis**:

> If '**wave-like**' **light** showed **particle properties** (photons), '**particles**' like **electrons** should be expected to show **wave-like properties**.

2) The **de Broglie equation** relates a **wave property** (**wavelength**, λ) to a **moving particle property** (**momentum**, *mv*). h = Planck's constant = 6.63×10^{-34} Js.

$$\lambda = \frac{h}{mv}$$

3) The **de Broglie wave** of a particle can be interpreted as a '**probability wave**'. You can use it to find the probability of finding an electron at a particular point (hmm, sounds familiar...).

4) Many physicists at the time **weren't very impressed** — his ideas were just **speculation**. But later experiments **confirmed** the wave nature of electrons.

I'm not impressed — this is just speculation. What do you think Dad?

The Evidence: **Electron Diffraction**

Electron diffraction patterns look like this

1) **Diffraction patterns** are observed when **accelerated electrons** in a vacuum tube **interact** with the **spaces** in a graphite **crystal**. As an electron hits a fluorescent screen, it causes a photon to be released, so you can see the diffraction pattern.

2) You can think of it in exactly the same way as photon diffraction. By summing the final phasor for every possible path, you can find how **likely** it is an electron will hit the fluorescent screen at a particular point. The **higher** the **probability**, the **brighter** the point on the screen.

3) The only difference is that when finding the **frequency** and **amplitude** of the electron phasor, *E* is the **kinetic energy** of the electron.

$$f = \frac{E_{kinetic}}{h}$$

4) This **confirms** that **electrons** show **quantum behaviour**.

5) This was a **huge** discovery. A few years earlier, **Louis de Broglie** had **hypothesised** that electrons would show **quantum behaviour** just like **light**, but this was the first **direct evidence** for it.

6) **Increase** the **electron speed** and the diffraction pattern circles **squash together** towards the **middle**.

   This fits in with the **de Broglie** equation above — if the **velocity** is **higher**, the **wavelength** is **shorter** and the **spread** of lines is **smaller**.

The Evidence: **Electron Interference** and **Superposition**

1) You can repeat experiments like **Young's double-slit** experiment with **electrons** too. They show the same kind of **interference** and **superposition** effects as you get with photons. As with the diffraction experiment, you usually show interference and superposition patterns using a fluorescent screen.

2) Just like photons, the **electrons try every path**:

> **Bright fringes** in an electron interference pattern show where the **probability** of an electron arriving is **high**. **Dark fringes** show where the **probability** of an electron hitting the screen is **low**.

Quantum Behaviour of Electrons

Electrons Don't show Quantum Behaviour All the Time

You **only** get **diffraction** if a particle interacts with an object of about the **same size** as its **de Broglie wavelength**.
A **tennis ball**, for example, with **mass 0.058 kg** and **speed 100 ms^{-1}** has a **de Broglie wavelength** of **10^{-34} m**.
That's **10^{19} times smaller** than the **nucleus** of an **atom**! There's nothing that small for it to interact with.

> *Example*   An electron of mass 9.11×10^{-31} kg is fired from an electron gun at 7×10^{6} ms^{-1}.
> What size object will the electron need to interact with in order to diffract?
>
> Momentum of electron = $mv = 6.38 \times 10^{-24}$ kg ms^{-1}
> $\lambda = h/mv = 6.63 \times 10^{-34} / 6.38 \times 10^{-24} = \boxed{1 \times 10^{-10} \text{ m}}$
>
> Only crystals with atom layer spacing around this size are likely to cause the diffraction of this electron.

A **shorter wavelength** gives **less diffraction effects**. This fact is used in the **electron microscope**.

> **Diffraction** effects **blur detail** on an image. If you want to **resolve tiny detail** in an **image**, you need a **shorter wavelength**. **Light** blurs out detail more than **electrons** do, so an **electron microscope** can resolve **finer detail** than a **light microscope**. They can let you look at things as tiny as a single strand of DNA... which is nice.

Practice Questions

Q1   Which observations show electrons to show quantum behaviour?

Q2   What happens to the de Broglie wavelength of a particle if its velocity increases?

Exam Questions

$h = 6.63 \times 10^{-34}$ Js ; $c = 3.00 \times 10^{8}$ ms^{-1} ; electron mass = 9.11×10^{-31} kg ; proton mass = $1840 \times$ electron mass

Q1   Electrons travelling at a speed of 3.5×10^{6} ms^{-1} exhibit quantum behaviour.

(a) Calculate the de Broglie wavelength of these electrons.   [2 marks]

(b) Calculate the speed of protons which would have the same wavelength as these electrons.   [2 marks]

(c) Both electrons and protons were accelerated from rest by the same potential difference.
Explain why they will have different wavelengths.
(Hint: if they're accelerated by the same p.d., they have the same K.E.)   [3 marks]

Q2   An electron has a kinetic energy of 9.6×10^{-16} J.

(a) Using the data above, calculate the speed of the electron.   [2 marks]

(b) Calculate the de Broglie wavelength of the electron.   [2 marks]

Don't look now, but... it's the ENDOFTHESECTION — YAY...

*Right — I think we'll all agree that quantum physics is a wee bit strange when you come to think about it. What it's saying is that electrons and photons aren't really waves, and they aren't really particles — they're **both**... at the **same time**. It's what quantum physicists like to call a 'juxtaposition of states'. Well they would, wouldn't they...*

Scalars and Vectors

Vectors are one of those things that are a bit annoying to deal with but are actually really useful. After all, what's the point in knowing how far you need to go if you don't know which direction to go in...

Scalars Only Have Size, but Vectors Have Size and Direction

1) A **scalar** has **no direction** — it's **just an amount** of something, like the **mass** of a **sack of meaty dog food**.

2) A **vector** has magnitude (**size**) and **direction** — like the **speed and direction** of next door's **cat** running away.

3) **Force** and **velocity** are both **vectors** — you need to know **which way** they're going as well as **how big** they are.

4) Here are a few examples to get you started:

Scalars	Vectors
mass, temperature, time, length, speed, energy	displacement, force, velocity, acceleration, momentum

Adding Vectors Involves Pythagoras and Trigonometry

Adding two or more vectors is called finding the **resultant** of them.
You find the resultant of two vectors by drawing them '**tip-to-tail**'.

Example

Jemima goes for a walk. She walks 3 m North and 4 m East. She has walked 7 m but she isn't 7 m from her starting point. Find the magnitude and direction of her displacement.

First, draw the vectors **tip-to-tail**. Then draw a line from the **tail** of the first vector to the **tip** of the last vector to give the **resultant**:
Because the vectors are at right angles, you get the **magnitude** of the resultant using Pythagoras:

$R^2 = 3^2 + 4^2 = 25$
So $R = 5$ m

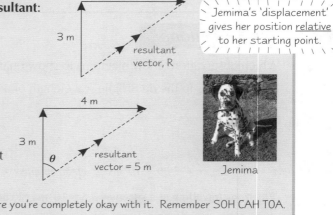

Jemima's 'displacement' gives her position <u>relative</u> to her starting point.

Now find the **bearing** of Jemima's new position from her original position.

You use the triangle again, but this time you need to use trigonometry. You know the opposite and the adjacent sides, so you need to use:

$\tan \theta = 4 / 3$

$\theta = 53.1°$ Trig's really useful in mechanics — so make sure you're completely okay with it. Remember SOH CAH TOA.

Jemima

Use the Same Method for Resultant Forces or Velocities

If the vectors aren't at right angles, you'll need to do a scale drawing.

Always start by drawing a diagram.

Example

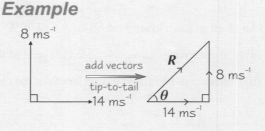

You know the resultant force is at 45° to the horizontal (since both forces are the same size).

So all you need to do is use Pythagoras:

$R^2 = 2^2 + 2^2 = 8$

which gives $R = 2.83$ N at 45° to the horizontal.

Don't forget to take the square root.

Example

8 ms⁻¹ ... add vectors tip-to-tail ... 14 ms⁻¹ ... R ... 8 ms⁻¹ ... θ ... 14 ms⁻¹

Start with: $R^2 = 14^2 + 8^2 = 260$
so you get: $R = 16.1$ ms⁻¹.
Then: $\tan \theta = 8/14 = 0.5714$

$\theta = 29.7°$

Scalars and Vectors

Sometimes you have to do it backwards.

It's Useful to Split a **Vector** into **Horizontal** and **Vertical Components**

This is the opposite of finding the resultant — you start from the resultant vector and split it into two **components** at right angles to each other. You're basically **working backwards** from the examples on the other page.

Resolving a vector v into horizontal and vertical components

You get the **horizontal** component v_x like this:

$$\cos \theta = v_x / v$$

$$\boxed{v_x = v \cos \theta}$$

...and the **vertical** component v_y like this:

$$\sin \theta = v_y / v$$

$$\boxed{v_y = v \sin \theta}$$

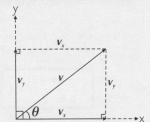

See pages 66 and 67 for more on resolving.

θ is measured anticlockwise from the horizontal.

Example

Charley's amazing floating home is travelling at a speed of 5 ms^{-1} at an angle of 60° up from the horizontal. Find the vertical and horizontal components.

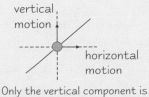

Charley's mobile home was the envy of all his friends.

The **horizontal** component v_x, is:
$$v_x = v \cos \theta = 5 \cos 60° = 2.5 \text{ ms}^{-1}$$
The vertical component v_y is:
$$v_y = v \sin \theta = 5 \sin 60° = 4.33 \text{ ms}^{-1}$$

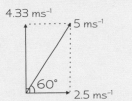

Resolving is dead useful because the two components of a vector **don't affect each other**. This means you can deal with the two directions **completely separately**.

Only the vertical component is affected by gravity.

Practice Questions

Q1 Explain the difference between a scalar quantity and a vector quantity.

Q2 Jemima has gone for a swim in a river which is flowing at 0.35 ms^{-1}. She swims at 0.18 ms^{-1} at right angles to the current. Show that her resultant velocity is 0.39 ms^{-1} at an angle of 27.2° to the current.

Q3 Jemima is pulling on her lead with a force of 40 N at an angle of 26° below the horizontal. Show that the horizontal component of this force is about 36 N.

Exam Questions

Q1 The wind is creating a horizontal force of 20 N on a falling rock of weight 75 N. Calculate the magnitude and direction of the resultant force. [2 marks]

Q2 A glider is travelling at a velocity of 20.0 ms^{-1} at an angle of 15° below the horizontal. Find the horizontal and vertical components of the glider's velocity. [2 marks]

His Dark Vectors Trilogy — displacement, velocity and acceleration...

Well there's nothing like starting the section on a high. And this is nothing like... yes, OK. Ahem. Make sure you've got to grips with how to resolve vectors... it gets even more fun when you get to resolve forces...

Motion with Constant Acceleration

If you think this is fun, wait 'til you get to the dizzy heights of 'F = ma' on page 68...

Uniform Acceleration is Constant Acceleration

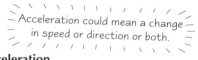

Acceleration could mean a change in speed or direction or both.

Uniform means **constant** here. It's nothing to do with what you wear.

There are **four main equations** that you use to solve problems involving **uniform acceleration**. You need to be able to **use** them **and** know how they're **derived**.

1) **Acceleration is the rate of change of velocity.**
From this definition you get:

$$a = \frac{(v-u)}{t} \quad \text{so} \quad \boxed{v = u + at}$$

where:

u = initial velocity $\quad a$ = acceleration
v = final velocity $\quad t$ = time taken

2) **s = average velocity × time**

If acceleration is constant, the average velocity is just the average of the initial and final velocities, so:

$$\boxed{s = \frac{(u+v)}{2} \times t} \quad s = \text{displacement}$$

3) Substitute the expression for v from equation 1 into equation 2 to give:

$$s = \frac{(u+u+at) \times t}{2} = \frac{2ut + at^2}{2} \qquad \boxed{s = ut + \tfrac{1}{2}at^2}$$

4) You can **derive** the fourth equation from equations **1** and **2**:

Use equation **1** in the form: $\quad a = \dfrac{v-u}{t}$

Multiply both sides by s, where: $\quad s = \dfrac{(u+v)}{2} \times t$

This gives us: $\quad as = \dfrac{(v-u)}{t} \times \dfrac{(u+v)t}{2}$

The t's on the right cancel, so: $\quad 2as = (v-u)(v+u)$

$$2as = v^2 - uv + uv - u^2$$

so: $\quad \boxed{v^2 = u^2 + 2as}$

Example

A tile falls from a roof 25 m high. Calculate its speed when it hits the ground and how long it takes to fall. Take **g = 9.8 ms⁻²**.

First of all, write out what you know:

$s = 25$ m

$u = 0$ ms⁻¹ since the tile's stationary to start with

$a = 9.8$ ms⁻² due to gravity

$v = ?$ $t = ?$

Usually you take upwards as the positive direction. In this question it's probably easier to take downwards as positive, so you get g = +9.8 ms⁻² instead of g = −9.8 ms⁻².

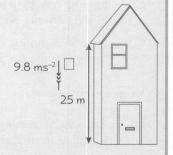

9.8 ms⁻²

25 m

Then, choose an equation with only **one unknown quantity**.

So start with $v^2 = u^2 + 2as$

$v^2 = 0 + 2 \times 9.8 \times 25$

$v^2 = 490$

$v = 22.1$ ms⁻¹

Now, find t using:

$s = ut + \tfrac{1}{2}at^2$

$25 = 0 + \tfrac{1}{2} \times 9.8 \times t^2 \implies$

$t^2 = \dfrac{25}{4.9}$

Final answers:

$t = 2.3$ s

$v = 22.1$ ms⁻¹

Motion with Constant Acceleration

Example

A car accelerates steadily from rest at a rate of 4.2 ms⁻² for 6 seconds.

a)   Calculate the final speed.

b)   Calculate the distance travelled in 6 seconds.

Remember — always start by writing down what you know.

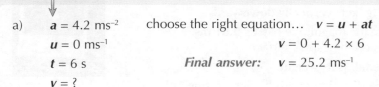

a) a = 4.2 ms⁻²   choose the right equation... $v = u + at$

u = 0 ms⁻¹ $v = 0 + 4.2 \times 6$

t = 6 s   **Final answer:** v = 25.2 ms⁻¹

v = ?

b) s = ?   you can use: $s = \dfrac{(u+v)t}{2}$ or: $s = ut + \frac{1}{2}at^2$

t = 6 s

u = 0 ms⁻¹

a = 4.2 ms⁻² $s = \dfrac{(0+25.2) \times 6}{2}$ $s = 0 + \frac{1}{2} \times 4.2 \times (6)^2$

v = 25.2 ms⁻¹

Final answer: s = 75.6 m s = 75.6 m

You Have to **Learn** the Constant Acceleration **Equations**

Make sure you learn the equations. There are only four of them and these questions are always dead easy marks in the exam, so you'd be daft as a brush in daft town not to learn them...

Practice Questions

Q1   Write out the four constant acceleration equations.

Q2   Show how the equation $s = ut + \frac{1}{2}at^2$ can be derived.

Exam Questions

Q1   A skydiver jumps from an aeroplane when it is flying horizontally. She accelerates due to gravity for 5 s.
(a) Calculate her maximum vertical velocity. (Assume no air resistance.)   [2 marks]
(b) How far does she fall in this time?   [2 marks]

Q2   A motorcyclist slows down uniformly as he approaches a red light. He takes 3.2 seconds to
come to a halt and travels 40 m in this time.
(a) How fast was he travelling initially?   [2 marks]
(b) Calculate his acceleration. (N.B. a negative value shows a deceleration.)   [2 marks]

Q3   A stream provides a constant acceleration of 6 ms⁻². A toy boat is pushed directly against the current
and then released from a point 1.2 m upstream from a small waterfall. Just before it reaches the waterfall,
it is travelling at a speed of 5 ms⁻¹.
(a) Find the initial velocity of the boat.   [2 marks]
(b) What is the maximum distance upstream from the waterfall the boat reaches?   [2 marks]

Constant acceleration — it'll end in tears...

If a question talks about "uniform" or "constant" acceleration, it's a dead giveaway they want you to use one of these equations. The tricky bit is working out which one to use — start every question by writing out what you know and what you need to know. That makes it much easier to see which equation you need. To be sure. Arrr.

Free Fall and Projectile Motion

Any object given an initial velocity and then left to move freely under gravity is a projectile.
If you're doing AS Maths, you've got all this to look forward to in M1 as well, quite likely. Fun for all the family.

Free Fall *is when there's Only* Gravity *and Nothing Else*

Free fall is defined as "the motion of an object undergoing an acceleration of '*g*'".
You need to remember:

1) Acceleration is a **vector quantity** — and '*g*' acts **vertically downwards**.

2) Unless you're given a different value, take the magnitude of **g** as **9.81 ms⁻²**, though it varies slightly at different points on the Earth's surface.

3) The **only force** acting on an object in free fall is its **weight**.

4) Objects can have an initial velocity in any direction and still undergo **free fall** as long as the **force** providing the initial velocity is **no longer acting**.

Kip thought he'd have a quick rest before he began his free fall...

You can Just Replace a with g in the Equations of Motion

You need to be able to work out **speeds**, **distances** and **times** for objects in **free fall**. Since **g** is a **constant acceleration** you can use the **constant acceleration equations**. But **g** acts downwards, so you need to be careful about directions.

To make it clear, there's a sign convention: **upwards is positive, downwards is negative**.

> **Sign Conventions — Learn Them:**
> **g** is always <u>downwards</u> so it's <u>usually negative</u>   **t** is <u>always positive</u>
> **u** and **v** can be either <u>positive or negative</u>   **s** can be either <u>positive or negative</u>

Case 1: No initial velocity (it just falls)
Initial velocity **u** = 0
Acceleration **a** = **g** = –9.81 ms⁻²
So the constant acceleration equations become: $\Rightarrow$

$$v = gt \qquad v^2 = 2gs$$
$$s = \frac{1}{2}gt^2 \qquad s = \frac{vt}{2}$$

Case 2: An initial velocity upwards (it's thrown up into the air)
The constant acceleration equations are just as normal,
but with **a** = **g** = –9.81 ms⁻²

Case 3: An initial velocity downwards (it's thrown down)
Example: Alex throws a stone down a cliff. She gives it a downwards velocity of 2 ms⁻¹.
It takes 3 s to reach the water below. How high is the cliff?   *s will be negative because the stone ends up further down than it started*

1) You know **u** = –2 ms⁻¹, **a** = **g** = –9.81 ms⁻² and **t** = 3 s. You need to find **s**.

2) Use $s = ut + \frac{1}{2}gt^2 = (-2 \times 3) + \left(\frac{1}{2} \times -9.81 \times 3^2\right) = -50.1$ m. **The cliff is 50.1 m high.**

Free Fall and Projectile Motion

You have to think of *Horizontal* and *Vertical* Motion *Separately*

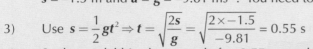

Example   Sharon fires a scale model of a TV talent show presenter horizontally with a velocity of 100 ms⁻¹ from 1.5 m above the ground. How long does it take to hit the ground, and how far does it travel horizontally? Assume the model acts as a particle, the ground is horizontal and there is no air resistance.

Think about vertical motion first:

1) It's **constant acceleration** under gravity...

2) You know $u = 0$ (no vertical velocity at first), $s = -1.5$ m and $a = g = -9.81$ ms⁻². You need to find t.

3) Use $s = \frac{1}{2}gt^2 \Rightarrow t = \sqrt{\frac{2s}{g}} = \sqrt{\frac{2 \times -1.5}{-9.81}} = 0.55$ s

4) So the model hits the ground after **0.55** seconds.

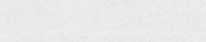

Then do the horizontal motion:

1) The horizontal motion isn't affected by gravity or any other force, so it moves at a **constant speed**.

2) That means you can just use good old **speed = distance / time**.

3) Now $v_h = 100$ ms⁻¹, $t = 0.55$ s and $a = 0$. You need to find s_h.

4) $s_h = v_h t = 100 \times 0.55 = \underline{55\ \text{m}}$

Where v_h is the horizontal velocity, and s_h is the horizontal distance travelled (rather than the height fallen).

It's *Slightly Trickier* if it *Starts Off* at an *Angle*

If something's projected at an angle (like, say, a javelin) you start off with both horizontal and vertical velocity:

Method:
1) Resolve the initial velocity into horizontal and vertical components.
2) Use the vertical component to work out how long it's in the air and/or how high it goes.
3) Use the horizontal component to work out how far it goes while it's in the air.

Practice Questions

Q1   What is the initial vertical velocity for an object projected horizontally with a velocity of 5 ms⁻¹?

Q2   How does the horizontal velocity of a free-falling object change with time?

Exam Questions

Q1   Jason stands on a vertical cliff edge throwing stones into the sea below.
He throws a stone horizontally with a velocity of 20 ms⁻¹, 560 m above sea level.
(a) How long does it take for the stone to hit the water from leaving Jason's hand?
Use g = 9.81 ms⁻² and ignore air resistance.   [2 marks]
(b) Find the distance of the stone from the base of the cliff when it hits the water.   [2 marks]

Q2   Robin fires an arrow into the air with a vertical velocity of 30 ms⁻¹, and a horizontal velocity of 20 ms⁻¹, from 1 m above the ground. Find the maximum height from the ground reached by his arrow.
Use g = 9.81 ms⁻² and ignore air resistance.   [3 marks]

It's not the falling that hurts — it's the being pelted with rotten vegetables... okay, okay...

The hardest bit with free fall questions is getting your signs right. Draw yourself a little diagram before you start doing any calculations, and label it with what you know and what you want to know. That can help you get the signs straight in your head. It also helps the person marking your paper if it's clear what your sign convention is. Always good.

Displacement-Time Graphs

Drawing graphs by hand — oh joy. You'd think examiners had never heard of the graphical calculator.
Ah well, until they manage to drag themselves out of the dark ages, you'll just have to grit your teeth and get on with it.

Acceleration *Means a* Curved Displacement-Time Graph

A graph of displacement against time for an **accelerating object** always produces a **curve**.
If the object is accelerating at a **uniform rate**, then the **rate of change** of the **gradient** will be constant.

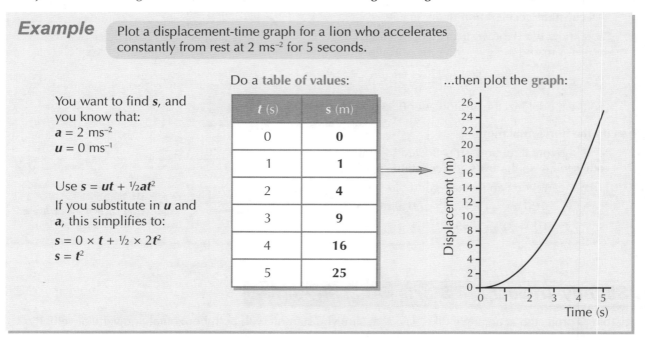

Example   Plot a displacement-time graph for a lion who accelerates constantly from rest at 2 ms⁻² for 5 seconds.

You want to find **s**, and you know that:
$a = 2$ ms⁻²
$u = 0$ ms⁻¹

Use $s = ut + \frac{1}{2}at^2$
If you substitute in **u** and **a**, this simplifies to:
$s = 0 \times t + \frac{1}{2} \times 2t^2$
$s = t^2$

Do a **table of values**:

t (s)	s (m)
0	0
1	1
2	4
3	9
4	16
5	25

...then plot the **graph**:

Different Accelerations Have **Different Gradients**

In the example above, if the lion has a **different acceleration** it'll change the **gradient** of the curve like this:

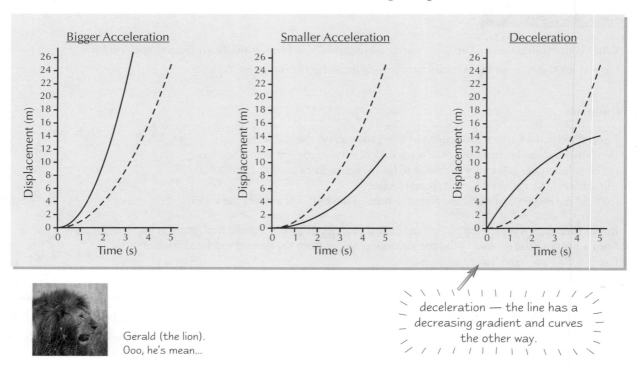

Bigger Acceleration   Smaller Acceleration   Deceleration

Gerald (the lion).
Ooo, he's mean...

deceleration — the line has a decreasing gradient and curves the other way.

Displacement-Time Graphs

The *Gradient* of a *Displacement-Time Graph* Tells You the *Velocity*

When the velocity is constant, the graph's a **straight line**.
Velocity is defined as...

$$\text{velocity} = \frac{\text{change in displacement}}{\text{time taken}}$$

On the graph, this is $\frac{\text{change in } y \, (\Delta y)}{\text{change in } x \, (\Delta x)}$, i.e. the gradient.

So to get the velocity from a displacement-time graph,
just find the gradient.

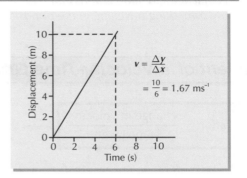

$$v = \frac{\Delta y}{\Delta x} = \frac{10}{6} = 1.67 \text{ ms}^{-1}$$

It's the Same with **Curved Graphs**

If the gradient **isn't constant** (i.e. if it's a curved
line), it means the object is **accelerating**.

To find the **velocity** at a certain point you
need to draw a **tangent** to the curve at
that point and find its gradient.

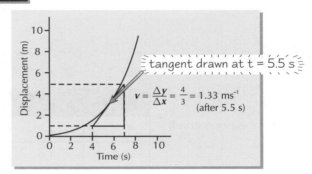

tangent drawn at t = 5.5 s

$$v = \frac{\Delta y}{\Delta x} = \frac{4}{3} = 1.33 \text{ ms}^{-1}$$
(after 5.5 s)

Practice Questions

Q1 What is given by the slope of a displacement-time graph?

Q2 Sketch a displacement-time graph to show: a) constant velocity, b) acceleration, c) deceleration

Exam Questions

Q1 Describe the motion of the cyclist as shown by the graph below. [4 marks]

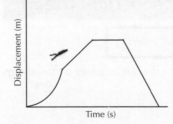

Q2 A baby crawls 5 m in 8 seconds at a constant velocity. She then rests for 5 seconds before crawling a further
3 m in 5 seconds. Finally, she makes her way back to her starting point in 10 seconds, travelling at a constant
speed all the way.
(a) Draw a displacement-time graph to show the baby's journey. [4 marks]
(b) Calculate her velocity at all the different stages of her journey. [2 marks]

Some curves are bigger than others...

*Whether it's a straight line or a curve, the steeper it is, the greater the velocity. There's nothing difficult about these graphs
— the main problem is that it's easy to get them muddled up with velocity-time graphs (next page). If in doubt, think about
the gradient — is it velocity or acceleration, is it changing (curve), is it constant (straight line), is it 0 (horizontal line)...*

Velocity-Time Graphs

Speed-time graphs and velocity-time graphs are pretty similar. The big difference is that velocity-time graphs can have a negative part to show something travelling in the opposite direction:

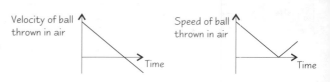

The **Gradient** of a **Velocity-Time Graph** tells you the **Acceleration**

$$acceleration = \frac{change\ in\ velocity}{time\ taken}$$

likewise for a speed-time graph

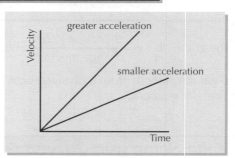

So the acceleration is just the **gradient** of a **velocity-time graph**.

1) **Uniform** acceleration is always a **straight line**.
2) The **steeper** the **gradient**, the **greater** the **acceleration**.

Example

A lion strolls along at 1.5 ms⁻¹ for 4 s and then accelerates uniformly at a rate of 2.5 ms⁻² for 4 s. Plot this information on a velocity-time graph.

So, for the first four seconds, the velocity is 1.5 ms⁻¹, then it increases by **2.5 ms⁻¹ every second**:

t (s)	v (ms⁻¹)
0 – 4	**1.5**
5	**4.0**
6	**6.5**
7	**9.0**
8	**11.5**

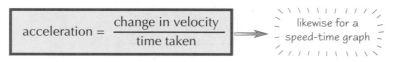

Humphrey (the lion)...

$$a = \frac{\Delta v}{t} = \frac{11.5 - 1.5}{4} = 2.5\ ms^{-2}$$

You can see that the **gradient of the line** is **constant** between 4 s and 8 s and has a value of 2.5 ms⁻², representing the **acceleration of the lion**.

Distance Travelled = **Area** under **Speed-Time Graph**

You know that:

$$distance\ travelled = average\ speed \times time$$

So you can find the distance travelled by working out the **area under a speed-time graph**.

Example

A racing car accelerates uniformly from rest to 40 ms⁻¹ in 10 s. It maintains this speed for a further 20 s before coming to rest by decelerating at a constant rate over the next 15 s. Draw a velocity-time graph for this journey and use it to calculate the total distance travelled by the racing car.

Split the **graph** up into **sections**: A, B and C
Calculate the **area** of each and **add** the three results together.
A: Area = ½ base × height = ½ × 10 × 40 = 200 m
B: Area = b × h = 20 × 40 = 800 m
C: Area = ½ b × h = ½ × 15 × 40 = 300 m
Total distance travelled = 1300 m

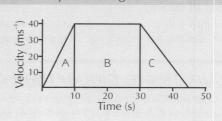

Velocity-Time Graphs

Non-Uniform Acceleration is a Curve on a V-T Graph

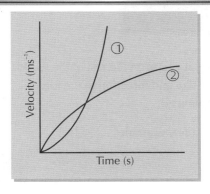

1) If the acceleration is changing, the gradient of the velocity-time graph will also be changing — so you **won't** get a **straight line**.

2) **Increasing acceleration** is shown by an **increasing gradient** — like in curve ①.

3) **Decreasing acceleration** is shown by a **decreasing gradient** — like in curve ②.

Simple enough...

You Can Draw Displacement-Time and Velocity-Time Graphs Using ICT

Instead of gathering distance and time data using **traditional methods**, e.g. a stopwatch and ruler, you can be a bit more **high-tech**.

A fairly **standard** piece of kit you can use for motion experiments is an **ultrasound position detector**. This is a type of **data-logger** that automatically records the **distance** of an object from the sensor several times a second.

If you attach one of these detectors to a computer with **graph-drawing software**, you can get **real-time** displacement-time and velocity-time graphs.

The main **advantages** of data-loggers over traditional methods are:

1) The data is more **accurate** — you don't have to allow for human reaction times.

2) Automatic systems have a much higher **sampling** rate than humans — most ultrasound position detectors can take a reading at least ten times every second.

3) You can see the data displayed in **real time**.

Practice Questions

Q1 How do you calculate acceleration from a velocity-time graph?

Q2 How do you calculate the distance travelled from a speed-time graph?

Q3 Sketch velocity-time graphs for constant velocity and constant acceleration.

Q4 Describe the main advantages of ICT over traditional methods for the collection and display of motion data.

Exam Question

Q1 A skier accelerates uniformly from rest at 2 ms^{-2} down a straight slope.

(a) Sketch a velocity-time graph for the first 5 s of his journey. [2 marks]

(b) Use a constant acceleration equation to calculate his displacement at t = 1, 2, 3, 4 and 5 s, and plot this information onto a displacement-time graph. [5 marks]

(c) Suggest another method of calculating the skier's distance travelled after each second and use this to check your answers to part (b). [2 marks]

Still awake — I'll give you five more minutes...

Having real-time velocity-time graphs might not sound the most thrilling thing in the world, but it is useful. Like when you're sat flying back from your hols, it's comforting to know the pilot knows how fast the plane's going and how far it is from the ground when trying to land. It makes the free peanuts taste so much nicer...

Forces

Remember the vector stuff from the beginning of the section... good, you're going to need it...

Free-Body Force Diagrams show All Forces on a Single Body

1) **Free-body force** diagrams show a **single body** on its own.

2) The diagram should include all the **forces** that **act on** the body, but **not** the **forces it exerts** on the rest of the world.

3) Remember **forces** are **vector quantities** and so the **arrow labels** should show the **size** and **direction** of the forces.

4) If a body is in **equilibrium** (i.e. not accelerating) the **forces** acting on it will be **balanced**.

Drawing free-body force diagrams isn't too hard — you just need practice. Here are a few **examples**:

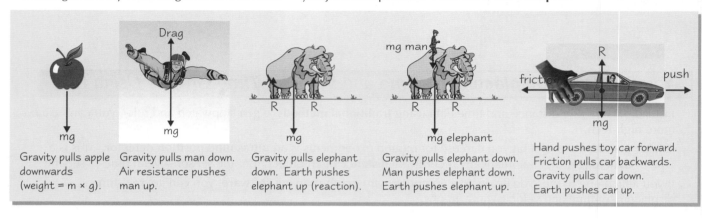

Gravity pulls apple downwards (weight = m × g).

Gravity pulls man down. Air resistance pushes man up.

Gravity pulls elephant down. Earth pushes elephant up (reaction).

Gravity pulls elephant down. Man pushes elephant down. Earth pushes elephant up.

Hand pushes toy car forward. Friction pulls car backwards. Gravity pulls car down. Earth pushes car up.

Resolving a Force means Splitting it into Components

1) Forces can be in **any direction**, so they're not always at right angles to each other. This is sometimes a bit **awkward** for **calculations**.

2) To make an 'awkward' force easier to deal with, you can think of it as **two separate forces**, acting at **right angles to each other**.

> The force **F** has exactly the same effect as the horizontal and vertical forces, F_H and F_V.
>
> Replacing **F** with F_H and F_V is called **resolving the force F**.

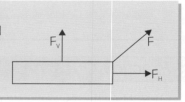

3) To find the size of a component force in a particular direction, you need to use trigonometry (see page 57). Forces are vectors, so you treat them in the same way as velocities — put them end to end.

So this...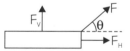

...could be drawn like this:

Using trig. you get:

$$\frac{F_H}{F} = \cos\theta \quad \text{or} \quad F_H = F\cos\theta$$

And:

$$\frac{F_V}{F} = \sin\theta \quad \text{or} \quad F_V = F\sin\theta$$

Example

A tree trunk is pulled along the ground by an elephant exerting a force of 1200 N at an angle of 25° to the horizontal. Calculate the components of this force in the horizontal and vertical directions.

Horizontal force = 1200 × cos 25° = **1088 N**
Vertical force = 1200 × sin 25° = **507 N**

Forces

You **Add** the **Components Back Together** to get the **Resultant Force**

1) If **two forces** act on an object, you find the **resultant** (total) **force** by adding the **vectors** together and creating a **closed triangle**, with the resultant force represented by the **third side**.

2) Forces are vectors (as you know), so you use **vector addition** — draw the forces as vector arrows put 'tail to top'.

3) Then it's yet more trigonometry to find the **angle** and the **length** of the third side.

Example

Two dung beetles roll a dung ball along the ground at constant velocity. Beetle A applies a force of 0.5 N northwards while beetle B exerts a force of only 0.2 N eastwards. What is the resultant force on the dung ball?

The resultant force is **0.54 N** at an angle of **21.8°** from North.

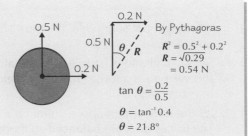

By Pythagoras
$$R^2 = 0.5^2 + 0.2^2$$
$$R = \sqrt{0.29}$$
$$= 0.54 \text{ N}$$

$$\tan \theta = \frac{0.2}{0.5}$$
$$\theta = \tan^{-1} 0.4$$
$$\theta = 21.8°$$

Choose sensible **Axes** for **Resolving**

Use directions that **make sense** for the situation you're dealing with. If you've got an object on a slope, choose your directions **along the slope** and **at right angles to it**. You can turn the paper to an angle if that helps.

Always choose sensible axes

Examiners like to call a slope an "inclined plane".

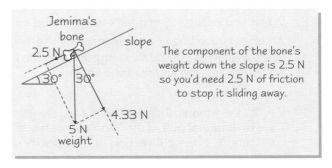

The component of the bone's weight down the slope is 2.5 N so you'd need 2.5 N of friction to stop it sliding away.

Practice Questions

Q1 Sketch a free-body force diagram for an ice hockey puck moving across the ice (assuming no friction).

Q2 What are the horizontal and vertical components of the force F?

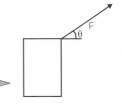

Exam Questions

Q1 A picture is suspended from a hook as shown in the diagram. Calculate the tension force, *T*, in the string.

[2 marks]

Q2 Two elephants pull a tree trunk as shown in the diagram. Calculate the resultant force on the tree trunk.

[2 marks]

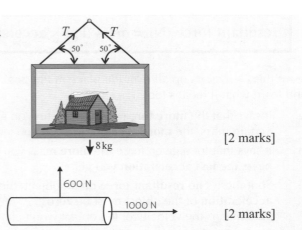

Free-body force diagram — sounds like something you'd get with a dance mat...

Remember those *F cos θ* and *F sin θ* bits. Write them on bits of paper and stick them to your wall. Scrawl them on your pillow. Tattoo them on your brain. Whatever it takes — you just **have to learn them**.

Forces and Acceleration

I know it's wrong to pick favourites... but F = ma is one of my favourite equations. It can tell you so much, from why the Moon orbits the Earth, to the force a bird poo will hit your head with on a fine summer's day...

You need a **Force** to **Change Velocity**

> If **no resultant force** acts on an object, its **velocity** will **not change**.

1) This might not sound like the most shocking statement you've ever heard, but in the 17th century it was outrageous.

2) So, say a giraffe is happily floating along at 2 ms⁻¹ with no resultant force acting on it — that's what it'll do **forever** unless a force changes its **velocity**. So you don't need a force for something to move — just to **change** its movement.

3) It's the same for an apple sitting on a table. The forces on it are **balanced** so there's **no resultant force** on the apple — it'll just stay sitting on the table until a resultant force (like when you pick it up) causes it to move, changing its velocity.

An apple sitting on a table won't go anywhere because the **forces** on it are **balanced**.

reaction (R) = **weight (mg)**
(force of table pushing apple up) (force of gravity pulling apple down)

4) When you change something's velocity, you either change its **speed**, its **direction** or **both**.

5) An object travelling in a **circle** may be travelling at a constant speed, but it is **constantly changing direction** — so its **velocity** is constantly changing too. The force that causes this change in velocity is a **centripetal force**, acting towards the centre of the circle.

> E.g. As the **Moon** orbits the **Earth** it travels at a **constant speed**. The **gravitational pull** of the Earth causes the Moon to continuously change **direction**, so its **velocity** changes too.

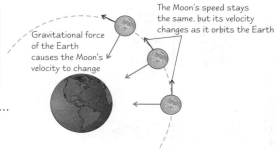
The Moon's speed stays the same, but its velocity changes as it orbits the Earth

Gravitational force of the Earth causes the Moon's velocity to change

Hmmm a change in velocity... that sounds like **acceleration** to me...

Newton's **2nd Law** says that **Acceleration** is **Proportional** to the Force

...which can be written as the well-known equation:

> **resultant force (N) = mass (kg) × acceleration (ms⁻²)**

$$F = m \times a$$

Learn this — it crops up all over the place in Physics.
And learn what it means too:

1) It says that the **more force** you have acting on a certain mass, the **more acceleration** you get.

2) It says that for a given force the **more mass** you have, the **less acceleration** you get.

3) So if there's **no resultant force** on an object, the **acceleration** of the object must be **zero**.
That means the velocity of the object won't change.
Nice when things all come together isn't it?

REMEMBER:
1) The **resultant force** is the **vector sum** of all the forces.
2) The force is **always** measured in **newtons**.
3) The **mass** is always measured in **kilograms**.
4) The **acceleration** is always in the **same direction** as the **resultant force** and is measured in **ms⁻²**.

Forces and Acceleration

All Objects Fall at the Same Rate (if you Ignore Air Resistance)

1) On Earth, the force that causes objects to accelerate towards the ground is the **gravitational pull** of the Earth. The gravitational field strength on Earth, g, is pretty much **constant** — so all objects should **accelerate** towards the ground at the **same rate**, no matter what their mass is.

2) Newton's 2nd law explains it neatly — consider two balls dropped at the same time — ball **1** being heavy, and ball **2** being light. Then use Newton's 2nd law to find their acceleration.

mass = m_1 resultant force = F_1 acceleration = a_1 By Newton's Second Law: $$F_1 = m_1 a_1$$ Ignoring air resistance, the only force acting on the ball is weight, given by $W_1 = m_1 g$ (where g = gravitational field strength = 9.81 Nkg^{-1}). So: $F_1 = m_1 a_1 = W_1 = m_1 g$ So: $m_1 a_1 = m_1 g$, then m_1 cancels out to give: $a_1 = g$	mass = m_2 resultant force = F_2 acceleration = a_2 By Newton's Second Law: $$F_2 = m_2 a_2$$ Ignoring air resistance, the only force acting on the ball is weight, given by $W_2 = m_2 g$ (where g = gravitational field strength = 9.81 Nkg^{-1}). So: $F_2 = m_2 a_2 = W_2 = m_2 g$ So: $m_2 a_2 = m_2 g$, then m_2 cancels out to give: $a_2 = g$

... in other words, the **acceleration** is **independent of the mass**.
It makes **no difference** whether the ball is **heavy or light**.
And I've kindly **hammered home the point** by showing you two almost identical examples.

Practice Questions

Q1 State Newton's 2nd law of motion, and explain what it means.

Q2 What is needed to change an object's velocity?

Exam Questions

Q1 A boat is moving across a river.
The engines provide a force of 500 N at right angles to the flow of the river and the boat experiences a drag of 100 N in the opposite direction. The force on the boat due to the flow of the river is 300 N.
The mass of the boat is 250 kg.
(a) Calculate the magnitude of the resultant force acting on the boat. [2 marks]
(b) Calculate the magnitude of the acceleration of the boat. [2 marks]

Q2 This question asks you to use Newton's second law to explain three situations.
(a) Two cars have different maximum accelerations.
What are the only two overall factors that determine the acceleration a car can have? [2 marks]
(b) Michael can always beat his younger brother Tom in a sprint, however short the distance.
Give two possible reasons for this. [2 marks]
(c) Michael and Tom are both keen on diving. They notice that they seem to take the same time to drop from the diving board to the water. Explain why this is the case. (Assume no air resistance.) [3 marks]

F = ma — Frighteningly macho armadillos...

These laws may not really fill you with a huge amount of excitement (and I could hardly blame you if they don't)... but it was pretty fantastic at the time — suddenly people actually understood how forces work, and how they affect motion. I mean arguably it was one of the most important scientific discoveries ever...

Work and Power

As everyone knows, work in Physics isn't like normal work. It's harder. Work also has a specific meaning that's to do with movement and forces. You'll have seen this at GCSE — it just comes up in more detail for AS level.

Work is Done Whenever Energy is Transferred

This table gives you some examples of **work being done** and the **energy changes** that happen.

1) Usually you need a force to move something because you're having to **overcome another force**.

2) The thing being moved has **kinetic energy** while it's **moving**.

3) The kinetic energy is transferred to **another form of energy** when the movement stops.

ACTIVITY	WORK DONE AGAINST	FINAL ENERGY FORM
Lifting up a box.	gravity	gravitational potential energy
Pushing a chair across a level floor.	friction	heat
Pushing two magnetic north poles together.	magnetic force	magnetic energy
Stretching a spring.	stiffness of spring	elastic potential energy

The word **'work'** in Physics means the **amount of energy transferred** from one form to another when a force causes a movement of some sort.

Work = Force × Distance

When a car tows a caravan, it applies a force to the caravan to moves it to where it's wanted. To **find out** how much **work** has been **done**, you need to use the **equation**:

> **work done (W) = force causing motion (F) × distance moved (s)**
> ...where W is measured in joules (J), F is measured in newtons (N) and s is measured in metres (m).

Points to remember:

1) **Work** is the **energy** that's been **changed** from one form to another — it's not necessarily the **total** energy. E.g. moving a book from a low shelf to a higher one will increase its gravitational potential energy, but it had some potential energy to start with. Here, the **work done** would be the **increase** in potential energy, **not the total** potential energy.

2) Remember the distance needs to be measured in metres — if you have **distance in centimetres or kilometres**, you need to **convert** it to metres first.

3) The force F will be a **fixed** value in any calculations, either because it's **constant** or because it's the **average** force.

4) The equation assumes that the **direction of the force** is the **same** as the **direction of movement**.

5) The equation gives you the **definition** of the joule (symbol J):
'One joule is the work done when a force of 1 newton moves an object through a distance of 1 metre'.

The Force isn't always in the Same Direction as the Movement

Sometimes the **direction of movement** is **different** from the **direction of the force**.

Example

1) To **calculate the work done** in a situation like the one on the right, you need to consider the **horizontal** and **vertical components** of the force.

2) The only **movement** is in the **horizontal** direction. This means the **vertical force** is not causing any motion (and hence not doing any work) — it's just **balancing** out some of the **weight**, meaning there's a **smaller reaction force**.

direction of force on sledge

rosebud

direction of motion

3) The horizontal force is causing the motion — so to **calculate** the **work done**, this is the **only force** you need to consider. Which means we get:

$$W = Fs \cos\theta$$

Where θ is the **angle** between the **direction of the force** and the **direction of motion**. See page 66 for more on resolving forces.

F

θ

$F \cos\theta$ → Direction of motion

Work and Power

Power = Work Done per Second

Power means many things in everyday speech, but in physics (of course!) it has a special meaning. Power is the **rate of doing work** — in other words it is the **amount of energy transformed** from one form to another **per second.** You **calculate power** from this equation:

Power (*P*) = work done (*W*) / time (*t*)
...where *P* is measured in watts (W), *W* is measured in joules (J) and *t* is measured in seconds (s)

The **watt** (symbol W) is defined as a **rate of energy transfer** equal to **1 joule per second** (Js⁻¹).
Yep, that's another **equation and definition** for you to **learn.**

Power is also Force × Velocity (P = Fv)

Sometimes, it's **easier** to use **this version** of the power equation. This is how you get it:
1) You **know** $P = W/t$.
2) You also **know** $W = Fs$, which gives $P = Fs/t$.
3) But $v = s/t$, which you can substitute into the above equation to give $P = Fv$.
4) It's easier to use this if you're given the **speed** in the question.
Learn this equation as a **shortcut** to link **power** and **speed.**

Example

A car is travelling at a speed of 10 ms⁻¹ and is kept going against the frictional force by a driving force of 500 N in the direction of motion. Find the power supplied by the engine to keep the car moving.

Use the shortcut $P = Fv$, which gives:
$P = 500 \times 10 = 5000$ W

If the force and motion are in different directions, you can replace *F* with $F \cos \theta$ to get: $P = Fv \cos \theta$

You **aren't** expected to **remember** this equation, but it's made up of bits that you **are supposed to know**, so be ready for the possibility of calculating **power** in a situation where the **direction of the force and direction of motion are different.**

Practice Questions

Q1 Write down the equation used to calculate work if the force and motion are in the same direction.
Q2 Write down the equation for work if the force is at an angle to the direction of motion.
Q3 Write down the equations relating (i) power and work and (ii) power and speed.

Exam Questions

Q1 A traditional narrowboat is drawn by a horse walking along the towpath. The horse pulls the boat at a constant speed between two locks which are 1500 m apart. The tension in the rope is 100 N at 40° to the direction of motion.

(a) How much work is done on the boat? [2 marks]
(b) The boat moves at 0.8 ms⁻¹. Calculate the power supplied to the boat in the direction of motion. [2 marks]

Q2 A motor is used to lift a 20 kg load a height of 3 m. (Take g = 9.81 Nkg⁻¹.)

(a) Calculate the work done in lifting the load. [2 marks]
(b) The speed of the load during the lift is 0.25 ms⁻¹. Calculate the power delivered by the motor. [2 marks]

Work — there's just no getting away from it...

Loads of equations to learn. Well, that's what you came here for, after all. Can't beat a good bit of equation-learning, as I've heard you say quietly to yourself when you think no one's listening. Aha, can't fool me. Ahahahahahahahahahahaha.

Conservation of Energy

Energy can never be lost. I repeat — energy can never be lost. Which is basically what I'm about to take up two whole pages saying. But that's, of course, because you need to do exam questions on this as well as understand the principle.

Learn the Principle of Conservation of Energy

The **principle of conservation of energy** says that:

> Energy **cannot be created** or **destroyed**. Energy **can be transferred** from one form to another but the total amount of energy in a closed system will not change.

Example

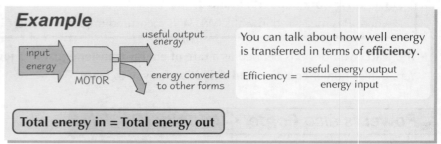

You can talk about how well energy is transferred in terms of **efficiency**.

$$\text{Efficiency} = \frac{\text{useful energy output}}{\text{energy input}}$$

Total energy in = Total energy out

You need it for Questions about Kinetic and Potential Energy

The principle of conservation of energy nearly always comes up when you're doing questions about changes between kinetic and potential energy.

A quick reminder:

1) **Kinetic energy** is energy of anything **moving**, which you work out from $E_k = \frac{1}{2}mv^2$, where v is the velocity it's travelling at and m is its mass.

2) There are **different types of potential energy** — e.g. gravitational and elastic.

3) **Gravitational potential energy** is the energy something gains if you lift it up. You work it out using: $\Delta E_p = mg\Delta h$, where m is the mass of the object, Δh is the height it is lifted and g is the gravitational field strength (9.81 Nkg^{-1} on Earth).

4) **Elastic potential energy** (elastic stored energy) is the energy you get in, say, a stretched rubber band or spring. If the object obeys Hooke's law (see p.26), you work this out using $E = \frac{1}{2}ke^2$, where e is the extension of the spring and k is the stiffness constant.

Examples

These pictures show you three **examples** of changes between kinetic and potential energy.

1) As Becky throws the **ball upwards**, **kinetic energy** is converted into **gravitational potential energy**. When it **comes down** again, that **gravitational potential** energy is **converted back** into **kinetic** energy.

2) As Dominic goes **down the slide**, **gravitational potential energy** is converted to **kinetic energy**.

3) As Simon bounces upwards from the trampoline, **elastic potential energy** is converted to **kinetic energy**, to **gravitational potential energy**. As he comes back down again, that **gravitational potential** energy is **converted back** to **kinetic** energy, to **elastic potential** energy, and so on.

> In **real life** there are also **frictional forces** — Simon would have to use some **force** from his **muscles** to keep **jumping** to the **same height** above the trampoline each time. Each time the trampoline **stretches**, some **heat** is generated in the trampoline material. You're usually told to **ignore friction** in exam questions — this means you can **assume** that the **only forces** are those that provide the **potential or kinetic energy** (in this example that's **Simon's weight** and the **tension** in the springs and trampoline material).
> If you're ignoring friction, you can say that the **sum of the kinetic and potential energies is constant**.

Conservation of Energy

Use Conservation of Energy to **Solve Problems**

You need to be able to **use** conservation of mechanical energy (change in potential energy = change in kinetic energy) to solve problems. The classic example is the **simple pendulum**.

In a simple pendulum, you assume that all the mass is in the **bob** at the end.

Example

A simple pendulum has a mass of 700 g and a length of 50 cm. It is pulled out to an angle of 30° from the vertical.

(a) Find the gravitational potential energy stored in the pendulum bob.

Start by drawing a diagram.

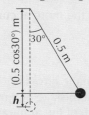

You can work out the increase in height, **h**, of the end of the pendulum using trig.

Gravitational potential energy = **mgh**
= 0.7 × 9.81 × (0.5 − 0.5 cos30°)
= 0.46 J

(b) The pendulum is released. Find the maximum speed of the pendulum bob as it passes the vertical position.

To find the *maximum* speed, assume no air resistance, then **mgh** = ½**mv²**.

So $\frac{1}{2}mv^2 = 0.46$

rearrange to find $v = \sqrt{\dfrac{2 \times 0.46}{0.7}} = 1.15$ ms⁻¹

OR

Cancel the **m**s and rearrange to give:
$v^2 = 2gh$
= 2 × 9.81 × (0.5 − 0.5 cos30°)
= 1.31429...
$v = 1.15$ ms⁻¹

You could be asked to apply this stuff to just about any situation in the exam. **Rollercoasters** are a bit of a favourite.

Practice Questions

Q1 State the principle of conservation of energy.

Q2 What are the equations for calculating kinetic energy and gravitational potential energy?

Q3 Show that, if there's no air resistance and the mass of the string is negligible, the speed of a pendulum is independent of the mass of the bob.

Exam Questions

Q1 A skateboarder is on a half-pipe. He lets the board run down one side of the ramp and up the other. The height of the ramp is 2 m. Take **g** as 9.81 Nkg⁻¹.

(a) If you assume that there is no friction, what would be his speed at the lowest point of the ramp? [3 marks]

(b) How high will he rise up the other side? [1 mark]

(c) Real ramps are not frictionless, so what must the skater do to reach the top on the other side? [1 mark]

Q2 A 20 g rubber ball is released from a height of 8 m. (Assume that the effect of air resistance is negligible.)

(a) Find the kinetic energy of the ball just before it hits the ground. [2 marks]

(b) The ball strikes the ground and rebounds to a height of 6.5 m. How much energy is converted to heat and sound in the impact with the ground? [2 marks]

Energy is never lost — it just sometimes prefers the scenic route...

Remember to check your answers — I can't count the number of times I've forgotten to square the velocities or to multiply by the ½... I reckon it's definitely worth the extra minute to check.

Error Analysis

Science is all about getting good evidence to test your theories... and part of that is knowing how good the results from an experiment are. Physicists always have to include the uncertainty in a result, so you can see the range the actual value probably lies within. Dealing with error and uncertainty is an important skill, so those pesky examiners like to sneak in a couple of questions about it... but if you know your stuff you can get some easy marks.

Nothing is Certain

1) **Every** measurement you take has an **experimental uncertainty**. Say you've done something outrageous like measure the length of a piece of wire with a centimetre ruler. You might think you've measured its length as 30 cm, but at **best** you've probably measured it to be 30 ± **0.5** cm. And that's without taking into account any other errors that might be in your measurement...

2) The ± bit gives you the **range** in which the **true** length (the one you'd really like to know) probably lies — 30 ± 0.5 cm tells you the true length is very likely to lie in the range of 29.5 to 30.5 cm.

3) The smaller the uncertainty, the nearer your value must be to the true value, so the more **accurate** your result.

4) There are **two types** of **error** that cause experimental uncertainty:

Random errors

1) No matter how hard you try, you **can't get rid** of random errors.

2) They can just be down to **noise** (p.11), or that you're measuring a **random process** such as nuclear radiation emission.

3) You get random error in **any** measurement. If you measured the length of a wire 20 times, the chances are you'd get a **slightly different** value each time, e.g. due to your head being in a slightly different position when reading the scale.

4) It could be that you just can't keep controlled variables **exactly** the same throughout the experiment.

5) Or it could just be the wind was blowing in the wrong direction at the time...

Systematic errors

1) You get systematic errors not because you've made a mistake in a measurement — but because of the **apparatus** you're using, or your experimental method. E.g. using an inaccurate clock.

2) The problem is often that you **don't know they're there**. You've got to spot them first to have any chance of correcting for them.

3) Systematic errors usually **shift** all of your results to be too high or too low by the **same amount**. They're annoying, but there are things you can do to reduce them if you manage to spot them...

Lorraine thought getting an uncertainty of ± 0.1 A deserved a victory dance.

You Need to Know How to Improve Measurements

There are a few different ways you can **reduce** the uncertainty in your results:

Repeating measurements — by repeating a measurement **several times** and **averaging**, you reduce the **random uncertainty** in your result. The **more** measurements you average over, the **less error** you're likely to have.

Use higher precision apparatus — the **more precisely** you can measure something, the **less random error** there is in the measurement. So if you use more precise equipment — e.g. swapping a millimetre ruler for a micrometer to measure the diameter of a wire — you can instantly cut down the **random error** in your experiment.

Calibration — you can calibrate your apparatus by measuring a **known value**. If there's a **difference** between the **measured** and **known** value, you can use this to **correct** the inaccuracy of the apparatus, and so reduce your **systematic error**.

You can Calculate the Percentage Uncertainty in a Measurement

1) You might get asked to work out the percentage uncertainty in a measurement.

2) It's just working out a percentage, so nothing too tricky. It's just that sometimes you can get **the fear** as soon as you see the word uncertainty... but just keep your cool and you can pick up some easy marks.

Example

Tom finds the resistance of a filament lamp to be **5.0 ± 0.4** Ω.

The percentage uncertainty in the resistance measured $= \dfrac{0.4}{5.0} \times 100 = \mathbf{8\%}$

Error Analysis

You can Estimate Values by Averaging

You might be given a graph of information showing the results for many **repetitions** of the **same** experiment, and asked to estimate the true value and give an uncertainty in that value. Yuk. Here's how to go about it:

1) Estimate the true value by **averaging** the results you've been given.
   (Make sure you state whatever average it is you take, otherwise you might not get the mark.)

2) To get the uncertainty, you just need to look how far away from your average value the maximum and minimum values in the graph you've been given are.

Example — Estimating the resistance of a component

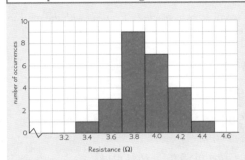

A class measure the resistance of a component and record their results on the bar chart shown. Estimate the resistance of the component, giving a suitable range of uncertainty in your answer.

There were 25 measurements, so taking the **mean**:

$$\frac{(3.4+(3.6\times3)+(3.8\times9)+(4.0\times7)+(4.2\times4)+4.4)}{25}=\frac{97.6}{25}=3.90\ (3\ \text{s.f.})$$

The maximum value found was 4.4 Ω, the minimum value was 3.4. Both values are both about 0.5 Ω from the average value, so the answer is **3.9 ± 0.5 Ω**.

Error Bars to Show Uncertainty on a Graph

1) Most of the time in science, you work out the uncertainty in your **final result** using the uncertainty in **each measurement** you make.

2) When you're plotting a graph, you show the uncertainty in a value by using **error bars** to show the range the point is likely to lie in.

3) You probably won't get asked to **plot** any error bars (phew...) — but you might need to **read off** a graph that has them.

\ \ \ \ \ \ \ \ | | / / / / / / /
Be careful — sometimes error bars are calculated using a set percentage of uncertainty for each measurement so will change depending on the measurement.
/ / / / / | | \ \ \ \ \ \

Example

Use the graph below to find the error in measuring the extension of material X.

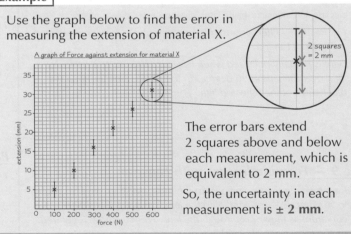

The error bars extend 2 squares above and below each measurement, which is equivalent to 2 mm.

So, the uncertainty in each measurement is **± 2 mm**.

You can Estimate the Uncertainty of the Graph's Gradient

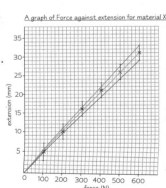

1) Normally when you draw a graph you'll want to find the gradient or intercept. E.g. for a force-extension graph, the gradient's 1/**k**, the stiffness constant of the material.

2) To find the value of **k**, you draw a nice line of best fit on the graph and calculate your answer from that. No problem there.

3) You can then draw the **maximum** and **minimum** slopes possible for the data through **all** of the error bars. By calculating the value of the gradient (or intercept) for these slopes, you can find maximum and minimum values the true answer is likely to lie between. And that's the **uncertainty** in your answer.

Random error in your favour — collect £200...

These pages should give you a fair idea of how to deal with errors... which are rather annoyingly in everything. Even if you're lucky enough to not get tested on this sort of thing in the exam, it's really useful to know for your lab coursework.

Answers

Unit 1: Section 1 — Imaging and Signalling

Page 5 — The Nature of Waves

1) a) Use $v = \lambda f$ and $f = 1 / T$

So $v = \lambda / T$, giving $\lambda = vT$ [1 mark]

$\lambda = 3 \ ms^{-1} \times 6 \ s = 18 \ m$ [1 mark]

The vertical movement of the buoy is irrelevant to this part of the question.

b) The trough to peak distance is twice the amplitude, so the amplitude is 0.6 m [1 mark]

Page 7 — Transverse Waves and Polarisation

1) a) [This question could equally well be answered using diagrams.]

For ordinary light, the EM field vibrates in all planes at right angles to the direction of travel. [1 mark]

Iceland spar acts as a polariser. [1 mark]

When light is shone through the first disc, it only allows through vibrations in one particular plane, so emerges less bright. [1 mark]

As the two crystals are rotated relative to each other there comes a point when the allowed planes are at right angles to each other. [1 mark]

So all the light is blocked. [1 mark]

Try to remember to say that for light and other EM waves it's the electric and magnetic <u>fields</u> that vibrate.

2) E.g. Polarising filters are used in photography to remove unwanted reflections [1 mark].

Light is partially polarised when it reflects so putting a polarising filter over the lens at 90 degrees to the plane of polarisation will block most of the reflected light. [1 mark].

Page 9 — Forming Images with Lenses

1) a) Rays meeting the lens parallel to the principal axis converge at the focal point. / Waves parallel to the lens axis are given spherical curvature as they pass through the lens. This curvature is centred on the focal point. [1 mark]
The focal length is the distance between the lens axis and the principal focus [1 mark].

b) $\dfrac{1}{v} = \dfrac{1}{u} + \dfrac{1}{f}$ so $\dfrac{1}{v} = -\dfrac{1}{0.2} + \dfrac{1}{0.15} = \dfrac{5}{3} \Rightarrow v = 0.6 \ m$ [1 mark]

2) a) $m = \dfrac{size \ of \ image}{size \ of \ object} = \dfrac{47.2}{12.5} = 3.776$ [1 mark]

b) $m = \dfrac{v}{u}$, giving $v = m \times u$ [1 mark]

$v = 3.776 \times 4 = 15.1 \ mm$ [1 mark]

c) $P = \dfrac{1}{f} = \dfrac{1}{v} - \dfrac{1}{u}$, so $P = \dfrac{1}{0.0151} - \left(-\dfrac{1}{0.004}\right) = 316 \ D$

Remember u is negative.

[3 marks for the correct answer, otherwise 1 mark for stating the correct equation and 1 further mark for some correct working]

Page 11 — Information in Images

1) a)

The diagram should show a fairly uniform mid-grey outside, with a lighter square in the centre. [1 mark]

b) Noise can be removed by replacing each pixel with the median of itself and the eight pixels surrounding it. [1 mark]

c)

100	99	100
97	100	98
101	101	98

[1 mark]

2) a) Number of bits = $log_2(65\ 536) = 16$ [1 mark]

b) $16 \div 8 = 2$ bytes [1 mark]

Page 13 — Sampling

1) $b = log_2\left(\dfrac{V_{total}}{V_{noise}}\right) = log_2\left(\dfrac{160}{10}\right) = log_2 16 = \textbf{4 bits}$ [2 marks for the correct answer, otherwise 1 mark for some correct working]

2) Minimum sampling rate = 2 × maximum frequency
= 2 × 500 = **1000 samples per second** [1 mark]

Page 15 — Signal Spectra and Bandwidth

1) a) Rate of transmission = samples per second × bits per sample
= 8000 × 8 = **64 000 bits per second** [1 mark]

b) 1 byte = 8 bits.
So, 64 000 bits per second = **8000 bytes per second**. [1 mark]

2) a) All the frequencies that make up the signal and their relative strengths. [1 mark]

b) 1400 − 200 = **1200 Hz** [1 mark]

Answers

Unit 1: Section 2 — Sensing

Page 17 — Charge, Current and Potential Difference

1) Time in seconds = $10 \times 60 = 600$ s.

Use the formula $I = Q / t$ [1 mark]

which gives you $I = 4500 / 600 = 7.5$ A [1 mark]

Write down the formula first. Don't forget the unit in your answer.

2) $W = VIt = 12 \times 48 \times 2 = 1152$ J [1 mark]

3) Work done = $0.75 \times$ electrical energy input

so the energy input will be $90 / 0.75 = 120$ J. [1 mark]

Rearrange the formula $V = W / Q$ to give $Q = W / V$ [1 mark]

so you get $Q = 120 / 12 = 10$ C. [1 mark]

The electrical energy input to a motor has to be greater than the work it does because motors are less than 100% efficient.

Page 19 — Resistance and Conductance

1) The sensitivity of the LDR is shown by the gradient of the graph [1 mark].

As the light intensity increases, the change in resistance per unit increase in light intensity decreases [1 mark].

So the sensitivity of the LDR decreases as light intensity increases [1 mark].

2)a) $R = V / I$ [1 mark]

$$= \frac{2}{2.67 \times 10^{-3}} = 749 \ \Omega \ [1 \text{ mark}]$$

b) Two further resistance calculations give 750 Ω for each answer [1 mark]

There is no significant change in resistance for different potential differences [1 mark]

Component is an ohmic conductor because its resistance is constant for different potential differences. [1 mark]

Page 21 — E.m.f. and Internal Resistance

1)a) Total resistance = $R + r = 4 + 0.8 = 4.8 \ \Omega$ [1 mark]

I = e.m.f./total resistance = $24/4.8 = 5$ A [1 mark]

b) $V = \varepsilon - Ir = 24 - 5 \times 0.8 = 20$ V [1 mark]

2)a) $\varepsilon = I(R + r)$, so $r = \varepsilon/I - R$ [1 mark]

$r = 500/(50 \times 10^{-3}) - 10 = 9990 \ \Omega$ [1 mark]

b) This is a very high internal resistance [1 mark]

So only small currents can be drawn, reducing the risk to the user [1 mark]

Page 23 — Conservation of Energy & Charge in Circuits

1)a) Resistance of parallel resistors:

$1/R_{parallel} = 1/6 + 1/3 = 1/2$

$R_{parallel} = 2 \ \Omega$ [1 mark]

Total resistance:

$R_{total} = 4 + R_{parallel} = 4 + 2 = 6 \ \Omega$ [1 mark]

b) $V = IR$, so rearranging $I_3 = V / R_{total}$ [1 mark]

$I_3 = 12 / 6 = 2$ A [1 mark]

c) $V = IR = 2 \times 4 = 8$ V [1 mark]

d) E.m.f. = sum of p.d.s in circuit, so $12 = 8 + V_{parallel}$

$V_{parallel} = 12 - 8 = 4$ V [1 mark]

e) Current = p.d. / resistance

$I_1 = 4 / 3 = 1.33$ A [1 mark]

$I_2 = 4 / 6 = 0.67$ A [1 mark]

Page 25 — The Potential Divider

1) Parallel circuit, so p.d. across both sets of resistors is 12 V.

a) $V_{AB} = \frac{1}{2} \times 12 = 6$ V [1 mark]

b) $V_{AC} = 2/3 \times 12 = 8$ V [1 mark]

c) $V_{BC} = V_{AC} - V_{AB} = 8 - 6 = 2$ V [1 mark]

2)a) $V_{AB} = 50/80 \times 12 = 7.5$ V [1 mark]

(ignore the 10 Ω — no current flows that way)

b) Total resistance of the parallel circuit:

$1/R_T = 1/50 + 1/(10 + 40) = 1/25$

$R_T = 25 \Omega$ [1 mark]

p.d. over the whole parallel arrangement = $25/55 \times 12 = 5.45$ V [1 mark]

p.d. across AB = $40/50 \times 5.45 = 4.36$ V [1 mark]

current through 40 Ω resistor = $V/R = 4.36/40 = 0.11$ A [1 mark]

Answers

Unit 1: Section 3 — Designer Materials

Page 27 — Hooke's Law

1) a) Force is proportional to extension.

   The force is 1.5 times as great, so the extension will also be 1.5 times the original value.
   Extension = 1.5 × 4.0 mm = 6.0 mm [1 mark]

   b) *F* = *ke* and so *k* = *F/e* [1 mark]

   k = 10 ÷ 4.0 × 10⁻³ = 2500 Nm⁻¹ [1 mark]

   There is one mark for rearranging the equation and another for getting the right numerical answer.

   c) One mark for any sensible point e.g.
   The string now stretches much further for small increases in force.
   When the string is loosened it is longer than at the start. [1 mark]

2) The rubber band does not obey Hooke's law [1 mark] because when the force is doubled from 2.5 N to 5 N, the extension increases by a factor of 2.3. [1 mark]

Page 29 — Stress, Strain and the Young Modulus

1) a) Area = $\pi d^2/4$ or πr^2.
   So area = $\pi \times (1 \times 10^{-3})^2/4 = 7.85 \times 10^{-7}$ m² [1 mark]

   b) Stress = force/area = $300/(7.85 \times 10^{-7}) = 3.82 \times 10^8$ Nm⁻² [1 mark]

   c) Strain = extension/length = $4 \times 10^{-3}/2.00 = 2 \times 10^{-3}$ [1 mark]

Page 31 — Structures of Solids

1) One mark for any composite material, one mark for a sensible application of that material, and one further mark for any sensible advantage of this material, e.g. reinforced concrete used in construction is stronger under tension than standard concrete; fibre-reinforced plastic (fibreglass) used in kayaks has a greater resistance to compressive and tensile forces than the plastic alone. [3 marks]

2) The height of the image is approximately 13.5 atoms. [1 mark]
   So the size of each atom is 4.05 ÷ 13.5 = 0.3 nm. [1 mark]

Page 33 — Mechanical Properties of Solids

1) a) A hard material is resistant to cutting, indentation and abrasion. [1 mark]
   Brittle materials break suddenly without deforming plastically. [1 mark]

   b) One mark for any sensible use e.g. a cutting instrument. [1 mark]
   One further mark for an explanation relating the use to the properties of hardened steel e.g. because the instrument would be able to cut through surfaces without getting damaged itself. [1 mark]

   c)

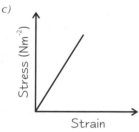

   [1 mark for correctly labelled axes, 1 mark for straight line through the origin]

2) E.g. The material would need to be stiff [1 mark] so that it would keep its shape and not crush the rider's head when a force was applied to it. [1 mark] It would also need to be tough [1 mark] so that it could absorb the energy of an impact without breaking. [1 mark] The material should be lightweight / have a low density [1 mark] so that it is comfortable for the rider to wear. [1 mark]

Page 35 — Electrical Properties of Solids

1) a) Copper wire is long, so the resistance along it will be large enough to measure. [1 mark] It also has a small cross-sectional area, which also increases its resistance. [1 mark]

   b)

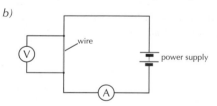

   [1 mark for sensible circuit diagram]
   Measure the length of the wire using a millimetre ruler and the diameter of the wire using a micrometer (to calculate the cross-sectional area)[1 mark]. Connect the wire in a circuit as shown above. (NB. You want the wires in the rest of the circuit to have as low a resistance as possible.) Measure the current that flows through the wire when a given potential difference is applied across it (e.g. 6 V). Use the equation V = IR to calculate the resistance of the wire. Then use the dimensions of the wire and the resistance measured to calculate the resistivity using the equation $\rho = \dfrac{RA}{l}$.
   [1 mark for a clear description of how to calculate the resistivity]

Answers

Unit 2: Section 1 — Waves and Quantum Behaviour

Page 37 — Superposition and Coherence

1)a) The frequencies and wavelengths of the two sources must be equal
[1 mark] and the phase difference must be constant.   [1 mark]

b) Interference will only be noticeable if the amplitudes of the two
waves are approximately equal.   [1 mark]

2)a) 180° (or 180° + 360n°).   [1 mark]

b) The phasors of the two points are equal in size/amplitude [1 mark]
but point in opposite directions. [1 mark]

Page 39 — Standing Waves

1)a)

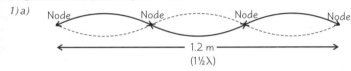

1.2 m
(1½λ)

[1 mark for the correct shape, 1 mark for labelling the length]

b) For a string vibrating at three times the fundamental frequency,
length = 3λ / 2

1.2 m = 3λ / 2

λ = 0.8 m [1 mark]

c) When the string forms a standing wave, its amplitude varies from a
maximum at the antinodes to zero at the nodes. [1 mark] In a
progressive wave all the points have the same amplitude. [1 mark]

Page 41 — Diffraction

1)   When a wavefront meets an obstacle, the waves will diffract round
the corners of the obstacle. When the obstacle is much bigger
than the wavelength, little diffraction occurs. In this case, the
mountain is much bigger than the wavelength of short-wave radio.
So the "shadow" where you cannot pick up short wave is very
long. [1 mark]

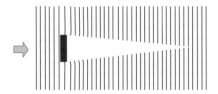

[1 mark]

When the obstacle is comparable in size to the wavelength, as it is
for the long-wave radio waves, more diffraction occurs. The
wavefront re-forms after a shorter distance, leaving a shorter
"shadow". [1 mark]

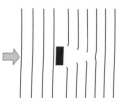

[1 mark]

Page 43 — Two-Source Interference

1)a)

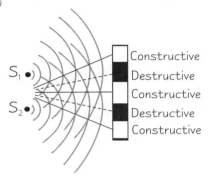

S_1
S_2

Constructive
Destructive
Constructive
Destructive
Constructive

[1 mark for correct constructive interference patterns,
1 mark for correct destructive interference patterns]

b) Light waves from separate sources are not coherent, as light is
emitted in random bursts of energy. To get coherent light the two
sets of waves must emerge from one source. [1 mark] A laser is
used because it emits coherent light that is all of one wavelength.
[1 mark]

2)a) $\lambda = v / f = 330 / 1320 = 0.25$ m.   [1 mark]

b) Separation = $X = \lambda D / d$ [1 mark]
= 0.25 m × 7 m / 1.5 m = 1.17 m. [1 mark]

Page 45 — Diffraction Gratings

1)a) Use $\sin \theta = n\lambda / d$

For the first order, $n = 1$

So, $\sin \theta = \lambda / d$ [1 mark]

No need to actually work out d. The number of lines per metre is 1 / d.
So you can simply multiply the wavelength by that.

$\sin \theta = 600 \times 10^{-9} \times 4 \times 10^5 = 0.24$

$\theta = 13.9°$ [1 mark]

For the second order, $n = 2$ and $\sin \theta = 2\lambda / d$. [1 mark]

You already have a value for λ / d. Just double it to get $\sin \theta$ for the
second order.

$\sin \theta = 0.48$

$\theta = 28.7°$ [1 mark]

b) No. Putting $n = 5$ into the equation gives a value of $\sin \theta$ of 1.2,
which is impossible.   [1 mark]

2) $\sin \theta = n\lambda / d$, so for the 1st order maximum, $\sin \theta = \lambda / d$ [1 mark]

$\sin 14.2° = \lambda \times 3.7 \times 10^5$

$\lambda = 663$ nm (or 6.63×10^{-7} m) [1 mark].

Page 47 — Light and Photons

1)   An electron needs to gain a certain amount of energy (the work
function energy) before it can leave the surface of the metal
(to overcome the bonds holding it to the metal). [1 mark]

If the energy carried by each photon is less than this work function
energy, no electrons will be emitted [1 mark]. Since energy
depends on the frequency, the photons are only energetic enough
to do this when the frequency of the incident light is above the
threshold frequency [1 mark].

Answers

Page 49 — Energy Levels and Photon Emission

1)a) The movement of an electron from a lower energy level to a higher energy level by absorbing energy. [1 mark]

b) $-2.18\times10^{-18} + 1.94\times10^{-18} = -2.40 \times 10^{-19}$ J.
This corresponds to $n = 3$. [1 mark]

c) $n = 3 \rightarrow n = 2$:
$-2.40\times10^{-19} - (-5.45\times10^{-19}) = 3.05\times10^{-19}$ J [1 mark]

$n = 2 \rightarrow n = 1$:
$-5.45\times10^{-19} - (-2.18\times10^{-18}) = 1.64\times10^{-18}$ J [1 mark]

$n = 3 \rightarrow n = 1$:
$-2.40\times10^{-19} - (-2.18\times10^{-18}) = 1.94\times10^{-18}$ J [1 mark]

Page 51 — The "Sum Over Paths" Theory

1) Probability $\propto$ (resultant phasor amplitude)^2 [1 mark]
Probability of electron reaching point A $\propto (6.3)^2 = 39.69$ [1 mark]
Probability of electron reaching point B $\propto (4.5)^2 = 20.25$ [1 mark]
$39.69 \div 20.25 = 1.96$, so an electron is almost twice as likely to reach point A as point B. [1 mark]

2) The frequency of phasor rotation = 6.0×10^{14} rotations per second.
Use time (s) = distance (m) $\div$ speed (ms^{-1}) to find the time taken for the photon to reach the detector.
$t = 0.12 \div c = 0.12 \div 3.0 \times 10^8 = 4.0 \times 10^{-10}$ s [1 mark]
So the number of phasor rotations along this path
$= f \times t = 6.0 \times 10^{14} \times 4.0 \times 10^{-10} = 2.4 \times 10^5$ rotations [1 mark]

3)a) $E_{kinetic} = \frac{1}{2}mv^2$ [1 mark]

$= \frac{1}{2} \times 9.1\times10^{-31} \times (4.0\times10^5)^2 = 7.3\times10^{-20}$ J (to 2 s.f.)

[1 mark]

b) $E = hf$ [1 mark]

$f = \frac{E}{h} = \frac{7.3\times10^{-20}}{6.6\times10^{-34}} = 1.1\times10^{14}$ Hz (to 2.s.f) [1 mark]

Page 53 — Using "Sum Over Paths"

1)a) i) By adding the phasors tip to tail, you can see the resultant is 1 cm long, giving an amplitude of 3. [1 mark]

resultant

ii) All the phasors line up in the same direction, so the resultant is three phasor lengths long, giving a resultant amplitude of $3 \times 3 = 9$. [1 mark]

b) Probability is proportional to the square of the resultant phasor amplitude. [1 mark]

So the probability of a photon reaching point D is nine times greater than the probability of a photon reaching point B. [1 mark]

Page 55 — Quantum Behaviour of Electrons

1)a) $\lambda = \frac{h}{mv}$ [1 mark]

$= \frac{6.63\times10^{-34}}{9.11\times10^{-31} \times 3.5\times10^6} = 2.08\times10^{-10}$ m [1 mark]

b) Either $v = \frac{h}{m\lambda}$ with $m_{proton} = 1840 \times m_{electron}$

or momentum of protons = momentum of electrons

$1840 \times m_e \times v_p = m_e \times 3.5\times10^6$

$v_p = 1900$ ms^{-1}

[1 mark for either method with correct substitution, 1 mark for correct answer]

c) The two have the same kinetic energy if the voltages are the same. The proton has a larger mass, so it will have a smaller speed. [1 mark] Kinetic energy is proportional to the square of the speed, while momentum is proportional to the speed, so they will have different momenta. [1 mark]
Wavelength depends on the momentum, so the wavelengths are different. [1 mark]

This is a really hard question. If you didn't get it right, make sure you understand the answer fully. Do the algebra if it helps.

2)a) $E_k = \frac{1}{2}mv^2$ [1 mark]

$9.6\times10^{-16} = \frac{1}{2} \times 9.11\times10^{-31} \times v^2$

$v = \sqrt{\frac{2 \times 9.6\times10^{-16}}{9.11\times10^{-31}}} = 4.6\times10^7$ ms^{-1} [1 mark]

b) $\lambda = \frac{h}{mv}$ [1 mark]

$= \frac{6.63\times10^{-34}}{9.11\times10^{-31} \times 4.6\times10^7} = 1.56\times10^{-11}$ m [1 mark]

$E_k = E_k$

$m\uparrow v^2\downarrow = m\downarrow v^2\uparrow$

So

a decrease in speed will mean a smaller wave

Answers

Unit 2: Section 2 — Space, Time and Motion

Page 57 — Scalars and Vectors

1) Start by drawing a diagram:

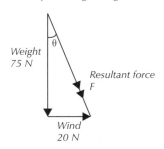

$F^2 = 20^2 + 75^2 = 6025$
So $F = 77.6$ N
$\tan\theta = 20 / 75 = 0.267$
So $\theta = 14.9°$
The resultant force on the rock is 77.6 N [1 mark]
at an angle of 14.9° [1 mark] to the vertical.

Make sure you know which angle you're finding — and label it on your diagram.

2) Again, start by drawing a diagram:

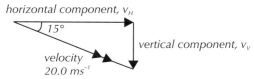

horizontal component $v_H = 20 \cos 15° = 19.3$ ms^{-1} [1 mark]
vertical component $v_v = 20 \sin 15° = 5.2$ ms^{-1} downwards [1 mark]

<u>Always</u> draw a diagram.

Page 59 — Motion with Constant Acceleration

1)a) $a = -9.81$ ms^{-2}, $t = 5$ s, $u = 0$ ms^{-1}, $v = ?$
use : $v = u + at$
$v = 0 + 5 \times -9.81$ [1 mark for either step of working]
$v = -49.05$ ms^{-1} [1 mark]

NB: It's negative because she's falling downwards and we took upwards as the positive direction.

b) Use: $s = \left(\dfrac{u+v}{2}\right)t$ or $s = ut + ½ at^2$ [1 mark for either]

$s = \dfrac{-49.05}{2} \times 5$ $s = 0 + ½ \times -9.81 \times 5^2$

$s = -122.625$ m $s = -122.625$ m
So she fell 122.625 m   [1 mark for answer]

2)a) $v = 0$ ms^{-1}, $t = 3.2$ s, $s = 40$ m, $u = ?$

use: $s = \left(\dfrac{u+v}{2}\right)t$ [1 mark]

$40 = 3.2u \div 2$

$u = \dfrac{80}{3.2} = 25$ ms^{-1} [1 mark]

b) use: $v^2 = u^2 + 2as$ [1 mark]
$0 = 25^2 + 80a$
$-80a = 625$
$a = -7.8$ ms^{-2} [1 mark]

3)a) Take upstream as negative: $v = 5$ ms^{-1}, $a = 6$ ms^{-2}, $s = 1.2$ m, $u = ?$
use: $v^2 = u^2 + 2as$ [1 mark]

$5^2 = u^2 + 2 \times 6 \times 1.2$
$u^2 = 25 - 14.4 = 10.6$
$u = -3.26$ ms^{-1} [1 mark]

b) From furthest point: $u = 0$ ms^{-1}, $a = 6$ ms^{-2}, $v = 5$ ms^{-1}, $s = ?$
use: $v^2 = u^2 + 2as$ [1 mark]

$5^2 = 0 + 2 \times 6 \times s$
$s = 25 \div 12 = 2.08$ m [1 mark]

Page 61 — Free Fall and Projectile Motion

1)a) You only need to worry about the vertical motion of the stone.
$u = 0$ ms^{-1}, $s = -560$ m, $a = -g = -9.81$ ms^{-2}, $t = ?$
You need to find t, so use: $s = ut + ½ at^2$ [1 mark]
$-560 = 0 + ½ \times -9.81 \times t^2$

$t = \sqrt{\dfrac{2 \times (-560)}{-9.81}} = 10.7$ s (1 d.p.) = 11 s (to the nearest second)

[1 mark]

b) You know that in the horizontal direction:
$v = 20$ m/s, $t = 10.7$ s, $a = 0$, $s = ?$

So use velocity $= \dfrac{distance}{time}$, $v = \dfrac{s}{t}$ [1 mark]
$s = v \times t = 20 \times 10.7 = 214$ m (to the nearest metre) [1 mark]

2) You know that for the arrow's vertical motion (taking upwards as the positive direction):
$a = -9.81$ ms^{-2}, $u = 30$ ms^{-1} and the arrow will be at its highest point just before it starts falling back towards the ground, so $v = 0$ m/s.
$s = $ the distance travelled from the arrow's firing point
So use $v^2 = u^2 + 2as$ [1 mark]
$0 = 30^2 + 2 \times -9.81 \times s$

$900 = 2 \times 9.81s$

$s = \dfrac{900}{2 \times 9.81} = 45.9$ m [1 mark]

So the maximum distance reached from the ground
$= 45.9 + 1 = 47$ m (to the nearest metre). [1 mark]

Answers

Page 63 — Displacement-Time Graphs

1) Split graph into four sections:

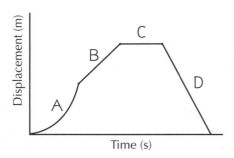

A: acceleration [1 mark]

B: constant velocity [1 mark]

C: stationary [1 mark]

D: constant velocity in opposite direction to A and B [1 mark]

2) a)

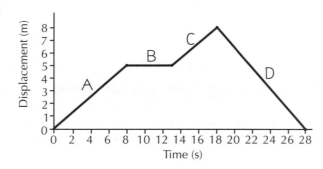

[4 marks — 1 mark for each section correctly drawn]

b) At A: $v = \dfrac{\text{displacement}}{\text{time}} = \dfrac{5}{8} = 0.625\ ms^{-1}$

At B: $v = 0$

At C: $v = \dfrac{\text{displacement}}{\text{time}} = \dfrac{3}{5} = 0.6\ ms^{-1}$

At D: $v = \dfrac{\text{displacement}}{\text{time}} = \dfrac{-8}{10} = -0.8\ ms^{-1}$

[2 marks for all correct or just 1 mark for 2 or 3 correct]

Page 65 — Velocity-Time Graphs

1) a)

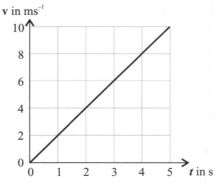

[2 marks]

b) use $s = ut + \tfrac{1}{2}at^2$ [1 mark]

$t = 1, s = 1$

$t = 2, s = 4$

$t = 3, s = 9$

$t = 4, s = 16$

$t = 5, s = 25$

[2 marks for all correct or 1 mark for at least 3 pairs of values right]

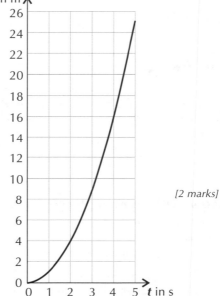

[2 marks]

c) E.g. another way to calculate displacement is to find the area under the velocity-time graph. [1 mark]

E.g. total displacement = $\tfrac{1}{2} \times 5 \times 10 = 25\ m$ [1 mark]

Answers

Page 67 — Forces

1)

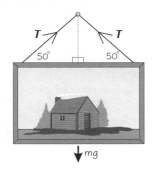

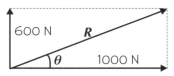

Weight = vertical component of tension × 2
$8 \times 9.81 = 2T \sin50°$ *[1 mark]*
$78.48 = 0.766 \times 2T$
$102.45 = 2T$
$T = 51.2$ N *[1 mark]*

2)

By Pythagoras:
$R = \sqrt{1000^2 + 600^2} = 1166$ N *[1 mark]*

$\tan\theta = \dfrac{600}{1000}$, so $\theta = \tan^{-1} 0.6 = 31.0°$ *[1 mark]*

Page 69 — Forces and Acceleration

1)a) Force perpendicular to river flow = 500 – 100 = 400 N *[1 mark]*
Force parallel to river flow = 300 N

Resultant force = $\sqrt{400^2 + 300^2} = 500$ N *[1 mark]*

b) $a = F/m$ (from $F = ma$) *[1 mark]*
= 500/250 = 2 ms^{-2} *[1 mark]*

2)a) The resultant force acting on it *[1 mark]* and its mass. *[1 mark]*

b) Michael is able to exert a greater force than Tom.
Michael is lighter than Tom. *[1 mark each for 2 sensible points]*

c) The only force acting on each of them is their weight = mg
[1 mark].
Since $F = ma$, this gives $ma = mg$, or $a = g$ *[1 mark]*.
Their acceleration doesn't depend on their mass — it's the same for both of them — so they reach the water at the same time.
[1 mark]

Page 71 — Work and Power

1)a)

Force in direction of travel = 100 cos40° = 76.6 N *[1 mark]*
$W = Fs = 76.6 \times 1500 = 114\,900$ J *[1 mark]*

b) Use $P = Fv$ *[1 mark]*
= 100 cos40° × 0.8 = 61.3 W *[1 mark]*

2)a) Use $W = Fs$ *[1 mark]*
= 20 × 9.81 × 3 = 588.6 J *[1 mark]*

Remember that 20 kg is not the force — it's the mass. So you need to multiply it by 9.81 Nkg^{-1} to get the weight.

b) Use $P = Fv$ *[1 mark]*
= 20 × 9.81 × 0.25 = 49.05 W *[1 mark]*

Page 73 — Conservation of Energy

1)a) Use $E_k = \frac{1}{2}mv^2$ and $E_p = mgh$ *[1 mark]*
$\frac{1}{2}mv^2 = mgh$
$\frac{1}{2}v^2 = gh$
$v^2 = 2gh = 2 \times 9.81 \times 2 = 39.24$ *[1 mark]*
$v = 6.26$ ms^{-1} *[1 mark]*

'No friction' allows you to say that the changes in kinetic and potential energy will be the same.

b) 2 m — no friction means the kinetic energy will all change back into potential energy, so he will rise back up to the same height as he started. *[1 mark]*

c) Put in some more energy by actively 'skating'. *[1 mark]*

2)a) If there's no air resistance, $E_k = E_p = mgh$ *[1 mark]*
$E_k = 0.02 \times 9.81 \times 8 = 1.57$ J *[1 mark]*

b) If the ball rebounds to 6.5 m, it has gravitational potential energy:
$E_p = mgh = 0.02 \times 9.81 \times 6.5 = 1.28$ J *[1 mark]*
So 1.57 – 1.28 = 0.29 J is converted to other forms *[1 mark]*

Index

Index

Index